Monyhull 1908 - 1998

A History of Caring

By Deborah Hutchings

This Book Is Dedicated To Everyone Who Has Lived And Worked At Monyhull Over The Years

MONYHULL 1908 - 1998

A History of Caring

By Deborah Hutchings

Brewin Books

First Published by Brewin Books,
Studley, Warwickshire B80 7LG
in 1998

ISBN 1 85858 131 1

British Library Cataloguing in Publication Data
A Catalogue record for this book is available
from the British Library

Typeset in Caxton Book
and printed by
Heron Press, Kings Norton, Birmingham

Foreword

Too many people have been hidden from history for too long. The lives, actions and thoughts of most women, the poor, the working class, the lower middle class and ethnic minorities have been shrouded from our view by a want of evidence and, too often, by a lack of interest on the part of academic historians. Thankfully, since the 1960s this centuries-long trend has been countered by those historians who have followed the standard raised by E.P. Thompson. In the powerfully influential *The Making of the English Working Class* he called out that it was his intention to rescue the poor stockinger, the Luddite cropper, the obsolete handloom weaver and others from the enormous condescension of posterity.

The social historians who have followed Thompson's banner have striven to do four vital things. First they have struggled to find those who have been neglected and ignored in the past. Second they have sought to bring to the fore all those who have been excluded from historical enquiry. Third, they have endeavoured to hark to the voices of those who have not been heard. And fourth, they have battled to give status to those who have been decried and belittled. Deborah Hutchings stands firmly amongst those of us who believe in these principles. In *Monyhull 1908-1998. A History of Caring* she provides a valuable record of those folk whose abilities and dignity were ignored when they were categorised as 'feeble-minded' or 'sane epileptics'. Any prejudice against the people who lived in Monyhull will be dispelled swiftly by the words of those like Raymond Jordan. With no speech and very little use in his legs and arms, Raymond learned to use a typewriter by means of an attachment to his foot.

Monyhull 1908-1998 makes plain the talent and pride of Raymond and others, and it also proclaims the dedication of the majority of the staff who worked so hard to help those with learning disabilities. They included medical superintendents such as Dr Earl, who was far-sighted enough to see the person behind the label; charge nurses like Mr Reynolds, who initiated the Friends of Monyhull to buy extras for the lads on his ward; matrons of Miss Carse's ilk, who was at Monyhull for its first fourteen years and devoted herself to her responsibilities; and farm bailiffs such as William Fife, who was involved in the successful cultivation of the land around Monyhull.

This is an important book. It should be widely read, and when it has been read always hold close the words of Lily Miles. She died there sixty-five years later. Lily left home with an aching heart and many bitter tears she shed. She tried to bear her lot with content and appealed passionately, 'Oh dear friends, forget-me-not'. You have not been forgotten, Lily. You will live on.

Carl Chinn

Contents

Acknowledgements

This book could not have been written without the help and support of the staff and residents at Monyhull (both past and present) who passed on their stories and memories, old documents and photographs, to aid me in my research. I would like to express my gratitude to them all. Special thanks are given to Barry Ashton, Roland Clewley, George and Ena Cole, Alan and Jessie Hale, Fred Hill, and Dennis Homans, for sharing their time and experiences with me.

I would also like to pay tribute to the members of the Monyhull Book Editorial Committee, for their constant involvement and support in this project. In particular, I would like to thank Elizabeth Perkins, who had the initial idea to research and record the history of Monyhull before it closed, and who provided invaluable advice and guidance on all aspects of the book from beginning to end. Thanks also to Eileen McCann, for arranging and assisting with interviews, and for stories of days gone by; to Les Blennerhassett, for providing excellent source material and photographs; to Wynn Jones-Owen, for finding additional source material, and for providing the title of the book; to Revd. Siôr Coleman, for his continuous encouragement and assistance in proof reading; and to Miriam Wilcher, for her positive support and suggestions throughout. I am also grateful to Pat Roper, for all the help she has given in finding old records, documents and photographs, and the Revd. Dr. Brian Easter for his constant encouragement and support. A special thankyou goes to Alison Last, Chris Lloyd, and the team in the physiotherapy and occupational therapy departments, for their help, support, and cups of tea in times of great need!

My thanks also to the Birmingham Post and Mail, and the Local Studies and History Service, Birmingham Central Reference Library, for their kind permission to use photographs from their collections; to Dr. Carl Chinn, for writing the foreword to the book; and to Alan Brewin of Brewin Books, for his helpful suggestions and advice.

Finally, I would like to thank my family and friends for their constant support and encouragement over the last few months. Special thanks to Simon, for keeping me going, getting rid of my "writer's block" and generally helping me find my way.

Prologue

Monyhull Hall

Situated on a small hill, looking out over the grounds of the Monyhull site, with the Stratford-upon-Avon canal to the north, and Chinn Brook, the Dell, and the suburbs of the Maypole and Druids Heath to the south, stands Monyhull Hall. Three storeys high with a slate roof, it is known locally as the "White House". Today, in 1998, it is the administration building for the learning disability services, currently provided by South Birmingham Mental Health NHS Trust. Indeed, it has been used for this purpose for the last ninety years.

It seems there has been a house upon the Monyhull site for some nine hundred years. When William the Conqueror ordered a survey of all his lands to be recorded in the Domesday Book of 1086, Monyhull lay within the "berewick" or outlying estate of Kings Norton (then called Nortune), of the Manor of Bromsgrove. It was owned by a

Monyhull Hall, adapted as the administrative block, 1908.

Benedictine foundation, Westbury College (Westbury on Trym, Gloucester), which was established in the eighth century (Blennerhassett 1995). Monihill Manor, as it was then called, was surrounded by a moat, the traces of which can still be found today. A "Ketel De Monyhull" was listed as a tenant in Kings Norton during the reign of Henry III (1216 - 72), and the lay subsidy roll of 1275 mentions a Richard De Monhull. "Hull" is the Middle English term for hill (Lock undated).

Westbury College and its widely dispersed property, including Monyhull, was appropriated when Henry VIII set about dissolving the monasteries in 1538 to establish the Church of England. The King gave the "Manor of Monihills" to Sir Ralph Sadleir in 1543 (Goodger 1990). By 1590 it had become the home of William Sparry, whose family, as Roman Catholics, had been labelled as "recusants" for refusing to attend Church of England services. Penalties against Roman Catholics were incurred after the Gunpowder Plot of 1605. The Sparry family, like many important families of the time, were restricted to a life virtually under house arrest. They were also forbidden from entering public service or the learned professions (Goodger 1990). The family suffered greatly and burdened with debt after the death of his father, Daniel Sparry sold the manor in 1610 to William Child, with whose family the estate remained until the mid 18th century. It eventually passed into the hands of John Pountney and his sons, Richard and Humphrey.

A poster advertising the sale of "Money Hull Hall" dated Tuesday 6th September 1825, shows the estate at that time to have been the residence of "the late Mr Hicks", although the mansion and lands were "held by Mr Richard Pountney under a lease which expires on the 25th Day of March 1827". The sale was to be held by auction at the Hen and Chickens Hotel, New Street, Birmingham, and was advertised thus:

MONEY HULL HALL
WORCESTERSHIRE

TO BE SOLD BY AUCTION,
BY
J. E. & C. ROBINS,
(By Direction of the Executors of the late W. Hicks, Esq.)
At the House of Mr. WADDELL, the Hen and Chickens Hotel, in
New-Street, Birmingham.
ON TUESDAY, the 6th DAY of SEPTEMBER 1825,
AT FOUR O'CLOCK IN THE AFTERNOON.

MONEYHULL HALL

Was the Residence of the late Mr. HICKS, situate in the Parish of King's Norton, and County of Worcester, is a substantial and commodious Mansion, sufficiently extensive to form a distinct and respectable Residence for a Proprietor; consisting of the Hall, 18 feet by 18 feet, wainscoted Parlour, 18 feet by 13, Breakfast Room, Kitchen, Brewhouse, and Cellaring, four excellent Chambers, and four attics, Garden, Stabling, Gig House, & other Out-Buildings, independent of an excellent Farm House, with extensive and suitable attached Offices, Barns, Fold Yards, Cow Houses, Sheds, two Stables, Granary, and every other necessary and usual Outbuilding, all in most excellent Repair, and about 200 Acres of Land, of which upwards of 80 Acres are valuable Meadow and Pasture, in the Occupation of Mr. Richard Pountney, Lessee thereof until Lady-Day, 1827, except about 10 Acres in the Possession of the Proprietors of the Stratford Canal.

It is presumed the Public will deem it eligible to have the Whole offered in its compactness of Ring Fence, boundary Rights, and Liberties, in one Lot; but if not sold in this way, then the following.

LOT I
The HALL, Farm House, Buildings, Gardens, Orchards, and the under-mentioned Inclosures of very excellent Land, with the Ponds, Streams, and Floats.

No. on Plan	Names of Pieces	A. R. P.[1]	A. R. P.
1	Site of Buildings, Rick Yard, Garden, Orchard	3 2 9	
2	The Hall or Rye Grass Field	7 1 2	
3	The Long Meadow	3 0 9	
5	The Broad or Paradise Field	10 1 23	
6	The Fordrough Field	8 0 21	
7	The Green Field	7 3 3	
10	The Calves Close	4 3 19	
11	Barn Close	3 2 3	
12	Hall Meadow	7 0 37	
13	Harrison's Meadow	7 0 9	
14	Harrison's Close, next to the Bell Lane	6 3 37	
15	Harrison's Pasture Piece	7 0 21	
16	Harrison's Plough Ground	5 0 17	
17	Harrison's Field	5 2 29	
18	Harrison's Field, next to the Fordrough	6 3 9	
19	The Upper Garrats Field	7 0 17	
20	The Lower Garrats Field	8 0 2	
21	The Rough or Garrats Meadow	5 3 13	
22	The Dial Close	7 1 6	
23	The Dial or Dish Field	11 3 23	
24	The Rushy or Walker's Meadow	9 3 26	
25	The Money Hull Little Meadow	5 2 11	
31	The Fordrough	2 2 23	
	LOT II		
28	The Great Manuel Piece, near Mill Pool Hill, on the Birmingham and Alcester Turnpike Road	8 1 02	
30	The Upper Manuel Piece, next adjoining the Great Manuel Piece, also fronting the Birmingham and Alcester Turnpike Road	6 1 09	
29	The Middle Manuel Piece (Barley)	4 2 05	
27	The Lower Manuel Piece (Oats)	5 3 37	
			250 13

<table>
<tr><td></td><td colspan="2" align="center">LOT III</td><td></td></tr>
<tr><td>8</td><td>The Pound Ground, situate on
the Road leading from Money
Hull Hall towards King's Norton
Church, from which it is distant
about Half a Mile</td><td>11 0 02</td><td></td></tr>
<tr><td></td><td></td><td></td><td>11 0 02</td></tr>
<tr><td></td><td colspan="2" align="center">LOT IV</td><td></td></tr>
<tr><td>32</td><td>Parts of Paradise Meadow, Long
Meadow, Dial or Dish Field, and
the Manuels, taken by the Stratford
Canal Company for the Canal Towing
Path and other Purposes, with the
reserved Rental there from of
£31. 19s. 5d. and £1. 16s. 9d.
for Land-Tax, making together an
annual sum of £33. 16s. 2d.</td><td>10 0 24</td><td></td></tr>
<tr><td></td><td></td><td></td><td>10 0 24
199 008</td></tr>
</table>

LOTS 1, 2, and 3, comprising the Mansion and 188A, 3R, 24P of Land, are held by Mr. Richard Pountney, under a lease which expires on the 25th Day of March 1827, at the yearly Rent of £340. including other Lands for which several Rents of £4. 16s. 0d. a Year, and £10. a Year are paid by the Vendors to the Stratford Canal Co. (to wit) £4. 16s. 0d. for a piece of Land belonging to the said Company, called Hawke's Meadow, and £10 a Year for the Parts of Paradise Meadow, Long Meadow, and the Manuels, retaken by the Vendors, of the said Company, but which last mentioned sum of £10. a Year is set off against the like Amount, paid by the said Stratford Canal Co. for the use of Sough Water, arising out of the said Estate.

The above Estate is of good Quality, and ornamented with Oak and other Trees, Orcharding &c. is well supplied with Game, and has a Trout Stream and other Waters running through the Centre of the Estate, watering the Meadows &c.

The Distance by good Roads is, from Birmingham 5 Miles, Worcester 20, Stratford 18.

The Canal affords great Convenience in the Carriage of Manure &c. The Land-Tax is redeemed, a Modus of 3d. per Acre is paid in Lieu of Tythes, and the parochial Payments are very low.

For further Information apply to Mr. Harris, No. 1, Suffolk- Street; Mr. SIMPSON, Solicitor, Great Charles-Street; or the AUCTIONEERS, all of Birmingham.

The estate was finally sold in 1864 to Mr Ezra James Milward, a wealthy gun manufacturer living in Leamington. It would seem that Milward bought the estate and then demolished the Pountney house, building the Monyhull Hall that stands there today, as the building has been dated as being mid 19th century (Royal Commission on the Historical Monuments of England). The hall was set in 128 acres of land, with a lodge, cottage, stables, outbuildings, pleasure grounds and gardens, and remained as the Milward family residence for forty years. This was the last time Monyhull Hall was used as a private residence. In 1905 it became the property of the Birmingham, Aston, and King's Norton Joint Poor Law Establishment Committee "for the purpose of the provision and maintenance of Homes for the reception and treatment of sane epileptics and feebleminded persons". It was to be known as Monyhull Colony.

Chapter 1

Care and Control

Whilst Monyhull Hall had been changing hands over the centuries, English society had been undergoing its own upheavals, with far reaching consequences for people with impairments or disabilities. In the feudal society of the Domesday Book, the Lords of the Manor held the land which was lived on and farmed by peasants in small family groups. For the use of the land and the produce that the families were allowed to keep, the Lords would receive a tithe, or percentage of the produce as payment. If, for whatever reason, a member of the family were unable to contribute to the work, and the family were unable to care for or support them, then it was deemed that "the poor should be sustained by parsons, rectors and parishioners, so that no-one should die for lack of sustenance" (Carter 1911).

Medieval Society

As feudalism developed during the 13th and 14th centuries, towns became established as a "market place" where peasants exchanged their produce for money with which to pay rent to the Lords of the Manor . The seeds of a capitalist society were slowly being sown, and with it the growth of the merchant class as an intermediary between the work that was done and the profit that was gained. The Catholic Church had also become a powerful force in determining how people lived and was especially influential in the way that the poor and needy were perceived and treated. The Church provided alms (money, food, etc) to those who needed it, and funded the first "hospitality houses" as shelter for travellers, pilgrims and the infirm. The first infirmaries for lepers, and asylums for the insane were usually attached to a monastery, and so were initially religious and spiritual institutions (C.T.D.I. unpublished). Different types of institutions began to be established; leper houses, hospices for wayfarers and pilgrims, institutions for the "sick poor", and almshouses (Carlin 1989). None of these provided medical care as such. Some even excluded the very people who needed help. St. John's Hospital, Canterbury refused to admit pregnant women, lepers, the wounded, cripples, the insane, and those suffering from "falling sickness" (Bailey 1988). Three hospitals specialised in the care of people with learning disabilities and mental illness; the hospital of St. John the Baptist, Chester, was founded in 1232 "for the sustention of poor and silly persons", a hospital (name unknown) at Charing Cross, London, for the distraught and insane, and St. Mary Bethlehem or Bedlam as it became known (Knowles and Hadcock 1971). This care however, was little more than confinement.

At first, people were encouraged to give alms to beggars and to the Church. The Church of course benefited enormously, both in terms of the power to control institutions and the wealth that the hospitals and poor relief generated. Hospitals would be funded by the rich and wealthy, they were exempt from tax, and permanent residents were often required to turn over all of their possessions to the Church. Preference was given to those who could pay over those who could not. Misappropriation and abuse of hospital funds became a common feature of medieval hospitals and eventually led to their closure (Carlin 1989).

Vagrancy became one of the biggest problems facing society. Vagrants were people who travelled from place to place and who begged in order to survive. They were the people who for many different reasons were unable to work for a living; people with disabilities, the sick, the injured, the aged. Gradually, attitudes towards the poor and needy changed. They were perceived to be a threat to society, seen to be idle, deceptive, criminal and dangerous. The first Vagrancy Law - the Statute of Labourers, was passed in 1351, after the Black Plague had caused a drastic reduction in the population and the workforce. Workers began to demand higher wages and to travel around the country looking for better paid work, begging for alms on the way to support themselves. The statute made it illegal for people to give alms to the ablebodied. In 1388 it was made illegal to beg unless you had an impairment. Officials were to check whether beggars were genuine or not and documentation had to be carried for beggars to travel from place to place.

The Effects of the Reformation

The problem of vagrancy however, was on the increase. During the 16th century there was a rapid increase in the population, more unemployment due to labour intensive methods of work, and an increase in the numbers of injured and impaired as a consequence of war. When the monasteries were dissolved in 1538, and with them the monastery hospitals, more people than ever were forced onto the streets to beg. By 1555, authorised beggars (the sick, aged or impaired) had to be registered and were required to wear badges which allowed them to beg in certain areas.

The vagrancy laws culminated in the Elizabethan Poor Law of 1601. Overseers of the poor were appointed to collect poor taxes, remove vagrants to their places of birth, charge families with the care of those incapable of caring for themselves, and to administer the almshouses (C.T.D.I. unpublished). Yet the problem worsened. As the market economy developed, so the feudal system declined. The Enclosure Acts of the late 18th century meant that the people who had lived on and worked the land lost their rights, and masses of unemployed and homeless peasants headed for the towns in search of work. Combined with the effects of the Industrial Revolution at the end of the century, the towns soon became overpopulated, with appalling living and working conditions.

Workhouses and Asylums

The first workhouses for paupers were established in 1722. They were the last resort for the poor. Families were separated, allowed no visitors and lived in terrible conditions with barely enough food to live on. The Poor Law Amendment Act of 1834 prohibited support outside the workhouse for everyone except children, the sick, "defectives", the insane, and the aged and infirm, who were still allowed "outdoor relief". Hospitals at this time were divided into voluntary institutions funded by wealthy individuals or groups for the treatment of the acutely ill working and middle classes, and public hospitals for the treatment of the "sick poor". Those with chronic, incurable or terminal conditions were sent to the workhouse infirmaries. In 1871 the Poor Law Boards were replaced by Local Government Boards who began to put pressure on the local parishes to put more people into the workhouses. More workhouses had to be built, and separate provision began to be made for children, the aged, the insane and the impaired.

The Act for the Care and Treatment of Lunatics was brought before the Council of Birmingham in the summer of 1845. Winson Green Asylum (which became All Saints Hospital) opened in 1850. Earlswood Common, Redhill and the Midlands Counties Asylum, Knowle (which became Middlefield) were opened for "mental defectives" in 1855 and 1870 respectively. People with learning disabilities were labelled "mental defectives", "idiots", "imbeciles" and "feebleminded". They were legally distinguished from "lunatics" in the Idiots Act of 1886, which called for the local authorities to provide special asylums for them. However, the Lunacy Act of 1890 included "idiots" as well as "persons of unsound mind" and made no distinction between them for certification purposes. In 1881 only 3% of "known" mental defectives were receiving care in the new asylums that had been built for them (Smith 1960). Victorian society believed that these people needed to be protected from those who would exploit them, but more often than not was simply protecting itself. Mental illness and impairment were feared or regarded as something shameful, and the altruistic motives of the few were often tainted by the restrictive and punitive social beliefs of the time.

By the turn of the century, attention had become focused upon the plight of the "mental defectives", combined with alarm at what was perceived to be "criminal tendencies, their drunkenness and prolific breeding" (O'Hara 1967). In 1904, Lord Radnor's Royal Commission was appointed to investigate the "Care and Control of the Feebleminded". They were to consider the existing provision for mental defectives and to obtain information as to their numbers and conditions. Investigators were assigned to selected areas, to visit "all public elementary schools, poor law institutions, charitable establishments, training homes, reformatories, common lodging houses, prisons, idiot asylums, hospitals, and any establishment likely to harbour the mentally abnormal" (Tredgold and Soddy 1963). In 1906 it was estimated that there were 149,628 mental defectives in England and Wales, of which 6% were classed as "idiots", 18% as "imbeciles" and 76% as "feebleminded". The evidence presented exposed the "appalling living conditions of many defectives, and shocked public opinion into action to provide more institutional care and social supervision". The feebleminded were deemed to be a group "many times more numerous who need special training and care if they are to learn to adapt to society and to carry out useful employment." It was argued that special facilities were necessary. These were to be regarded "not just as a means of protecting the defective from uncontrolled behaviour, but as methods of promoting the happiness of the individual, by giving him some skill and opportunity to be of value to the community" (Tredgold 1906). The Commission recommended that the authorities should establish institutions or colonies for the provision of care and training of mental defectives.

Changes in the structure of society and the accompanying changes in attitudes have always determined the care and treatment of the "poor and needy". Over the centuries, those people who could not support themselves had variously been the objects of community and church charity, registered beggars forced onto the streets, and finally, segregated and confined in workhouses and asylums. The recommendations of the Royal Commission would likewise seal the fate of people with learning disabilities. For the next fifty years they were to be segregated from the rest of society in special institutions, ironically so that they could be "trained" to adapt to the very communities from which they were now to be excluded.

A Bold Venture

Whilst the Royal Commission was gathering together information for its reports, initiatives were already underway in the West Midlands. Mr. R. J. Curtis presented a paper at the West Midland Poor

Birmingham, Aston and King's Norton Joint Poor Law
Establishment Committee 1908

Law Conference in May 1901, in which he advocated the establishment of "Industrial Colonies, properly equipped and under medical supervision, where suitable cases could be properly treated and employed". As a result, the Birmingham, Aston and King's Norton Boards of Guardians decided to combine to form the Birmingham, Aston and King's Norton Joint Poor Law Establishment Committee. The purpose of this Committee was to provide accommodation for the "reception of Epileptic and Feebleminded persons not certified as Insane, and chargeable to one of the combined Unions". The Committee was formally constituted by Special Order on the 27th March 1905, and the following appointments were made:

Chairman	Mr. Henry James Sayer, J.P.
Vice-Chairman	Mr. William Brown
Clerk	Mr. Richard James Curtis

Birmingham Parish	Aston Union	King's Norton Union
Mr. J. H. Forrester, J.P.	Mr. W. M. Brown	Revd.G. Astbury, M.A.
Mr. H. J. Manton, J.P.	Mr. C. C. Cooke	Mr. Fred Barlow
Mr. A. J. Norton	Mr. A. H. James	Mr. T. A. Bayliss
Mr. H. J. Sayer, J.P.	Mr. G. Miller	Mr. A. Blackwell
Mr. J. R. Turner	Mr. T. O. Williams	Mr. J. Walter

The Committee proceedings (1905 - 06) reported that:

"The question of making more suitable provision for Epileptics who are now in Workhouses, and for Feebleminded persons, is one that has been much discussed during the past few years. Those engaged in the administration of Poor Law Relief are unanimous in the opinion that these classes should be dealt with in separate Institutions, in which proper and adequate classification, care, and treatment can be secured. Such Institutions are desirable in order that the Epileptic in his sane intervals may not be associated with imbeciles; that the feebleminded may not be put in depressing contact with the severer forms of the disease, and that both classes may have instruction and attention as may be best calculated to improve, if improvement is possible, and if not to render their lives as comfortable and as useful as their unfortunate conditions permit."

Scheme map of Monyhull Colony 1905

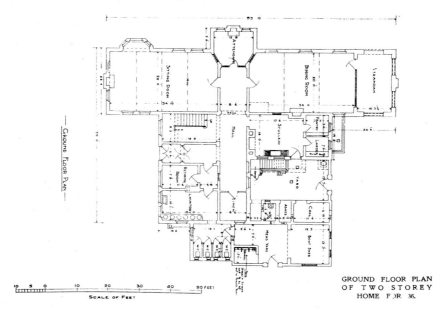

GROUND FLOOR PLAN
OF TWO STOREY
HOME FOR 36.

Ground floor plan of two storey home for 36 people.

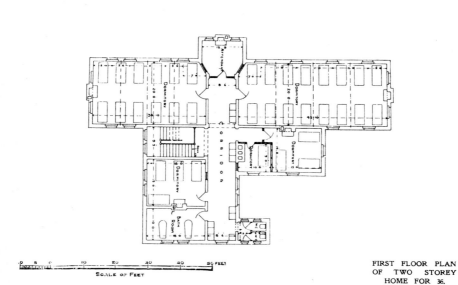

FIRST FLOOR PLAN
OF TWO STOREY
HOME FOR 36.

First floor plan of two storey home for 36 people.

At the very first meeting in April 1905, the Joint Committee decided to purchase the freehold estate of Monyhull Hall. The estate, comprising "a large dwelling house, together with a lodge, cottage, stable, and outbuildings, pleasure grounds, garden and land, having a total area of 128 acres" was purchased for the sum of £13,500 (inclusive of perpetual annual rents of £33. 16s. 2d.). Subsequently, the Kingswood Estate comprising farm house, farm buildings and about 46 acres of land was purchased for £5,500. The land "fronting to Monyhull Hall Road", of 10 3/4 acres was also purchased, for the sum of £1,600. The total estate then, consisted of nearly 185 acres of freehold land at a total cost of £20,600. It was bounded on the west side by the Monyhull Hall Road, on the east by the Alcester Road, on the north by the Stratford-upon-Avon Canal, and on the south by agricultural land.

It was agreed that accommodation should be first provided for 210 "inmates", of which 110 were from Birmingham, 50 from Aston, and 50 from Kings Norton. These excluded children under 16 years of age, "under the assumption that they would be dealt with by the City Education Committee", and "cases over 45 years of age" who were considered as "being less likely to improve".

The founding of the Colony was considered at the time to be a "bold venture". The Birmingham Committee were seen to be leading the way, and being one of the first of its kind, the scheme was approved of in instalments. The first of these was the building of "three Homes for Men and three for Women, four of these being one storey, and the remainder two stories in height, each Home accommodating 36 inmates giving a total of 216; a Laundry, capable of extension when necessary; a general Kitchen Block; a Cottage for Head Attendant, serving as Entrance Lodge, and adjoining which is a Weighbridge." The external design of the buildings was to be simple, using "common brick with a small quantity of stone dressing, and the roofs (are) covered with Broseley tiles". The building of detached houses or "homes" in different styles was an enormous step forward from the old style institutions. The original plans of the homes show the layout of both the one and two storey houses, with dormitories, bathroom, lavatories, sitting room, dining room, linen room, scullery, larder, pantry, coal and boot sheds. Monyhull Hall itself,

was to be altered and adapted as the administrative quarters, providing residence for the Matron and female members of staff, with an office, dispensary and stores. It was to be connected to the kitchen by a short covered walkway. Male members of staff were to reside in the old lodge, the gardeners cottage and Home 3, although most were to live outside the Colony.

In February 1906, Mr. Sayer and Mr. Curtis went before the Royal Commission to explain the Monyhull Colony scheme in detail. The Commission were greatly interested in the "experiment" and in June, Lord Radnor and other representatives of the Commission visited Birmingham, requesting a complete set of the plans and cost estimates to include in their report. Monyhull Colony was to act as a pioneer for the "care and treatment" of people with learning disabilities, and was to be copied by authorities all over the country.

MONYHULL COLONY
HOMES FOR EPILEPTICS & FEEBLE-MINDED.
ERECTED BY THE
BIRMINGHAM, ASTON, & KING'S NORTON,
JOINT POOR LAW ESTABLISHMENT COMMITTEE
OPENED ON THE 11th APRIL, 1908, BY
ALDERMAN H. J. SAYER. J.P.
LORD MAYOR OF BIRMINGHAM and
CHAIRMAN OF JOINT COMMITTEE.

MEMBERS OF COMMITTEE.
COUNCILLOR W. BROWN. *VICE CHAIRMAN.*
REV. CANON ASTBURY. M.A. *CHAIRMAN OF BUILDING COMMITTEE.*
T. O. WILLIAMS. *CHAIRMAN OF FINANCE COMMITTEE.*

F. BARLOW.	S. DOGGETT.	H. J. MANTON. J.P.
T. A. BAYLISS.	J. H. FORRESTER. J.P.	J. R. TURNER.
A. BLACKWELL.	F. JUCKES.	J. WALTER.
C. C. COOKE.	C. MILLER.	A. J. NORTON.
A. H. JAMES.		

R. J. CURTIS. *CLERK.*

C. WHITWELL & SON. *ARCHITECTS.*
THOMAS ROWBOTHAM. *BUILDER.*

Plaque unveiled at the opening of Monyhull Colony 11th April 1908.

Chapter 2

Monyhull Colony

Specialised institutions for the care and treatment of people with learning disabilities had been advocated by the Royal Commission as a means of protecting those seen to be at risk from exploitation and deprivation. They were also deemed necessary to protect society from those who did not conform to the strict social mores of the time. The eugenics movement had aroused fears that the nation would degenerate if the "feebleminded" were allowed to propagate freely, and segregation and even sterilisation were seen as viable solutions. This then was the backdrop against which the Board of Guardians set out to establish an industrial colony for the "epileptic and feebleminded."

Monyhull Colony was opened on the 11th April 1908 by Alderman H. J. Sayer, J.P., Lord Mayor of Birmingham and the Chairman of the Joint Committee. By December 1909 it had become the home of some 252 men and women from the Birmingham, Aston and King's Norton parishes, filling all of the then available accommodation.

Members of Staff

The resident staff employed by the Committee consisted of "a Matron, Assistant Matron (both of whom were trained nurses), Lady Book-Keeper, seven Female Attendants, three Assistant Female Attendants, Cook, Laundress, Assistant Laundress, Housemaid, Kitchenmaid, and Portress; Head Male Attendant, two Male Attendants, Handyman, and Gardener". The non-resident staff included the Medical Officer, Farm Bailiff, six Male Attendants, Tradesmen (Carpenter etc.) and the Farm Hands.

The first annual report of the Colony mentions the appointments of the Matron, Medical Officer and Chaplain:

"Miss M. J. Carse (Assistant Matron, Selly Oak Infirmary) was appointed Matron of the Colony in November 1907 and commenced duties in February 1908. In the interim she was much occupied in preparation for the equipment of the Colony. Miss Carse has proved herself to be a thoroughly capable administrator, and the Committee consider they were fortunate in securing her services at the initiation of the scheme."

"Dr. Bert Jordan, M.B., B.Ch., of King's Norton was appointed to the position of Medical Officer of the Colony. Dr. Jordan has had previous experience in dealing with epileptics and feebleminded persons in Poor Law institutions. The Medical Officer attends the Colony every other day and when called in by the Matron."

"From the opening of the Colony to June 1909, the Rev. Canon Barnard, Vicar of King's Norton, was Chaplain, and conducted a service every Sunday afternoon and gave a service or an address one evening weekly. He also attended monthly to administer Holy Communion. Upon Canon Barnard's leaving King's Norton, his successor, the Rev. Hugh Price was appointed Chaplain. The Free Church Council send a Minister to conduct services every Sunday evening. For the Roman Catholic members of the Colony services are provided in a room set apart in No. 1. Home."

The resolutions passed by the Committee from 1908 to 1909 recorded other staff appointments. Female Attendants included Miss E. A. Clarke, Miss Annie Loversidge, Miss D. Green, Miss S. Bloomfield, Miss Haslin and Miss J. Fisher, who were "appointed at the usual scale". Miss M. Nicol and Miss Leyland were appointed Assistant Female Attendants. The Committee also "resolved to confirm the appointment of Mr. W. Hipkiss of Barnsley Hall Asylum as Non Resident Male Attendant (Night) at a Salary and emoluments according to scale". The wages of the non resident male attendants were "fixed at 20/- per week with two meals per day, rising by increments of 1/- per annum to a maximum of 23/- per week, together with the same uniform provided for the Resident Staff." Martha Bannister was appointed as Laundrymaid "at a Salary after the rate of £20 per annum and emoluments be confirmed", and Miss Bertha Lewis was appointed as her assistant. Miss Lomas became the housemaid and Miss Smith, the kitchen maid, at a salary of £14 per annum.

Mr. Kennerley became the Chief Engineer; Mr Heskey was "permanently appointed as Carpenter at a wage of 36/- weekly, he to work 53 hours per week"; and Mr. Hollis was appointed as the Gardener. William Fife was the Farm Bailiff, and the Committee permanently appointed William Price as Farm hand "at wages in the same scale as the Non Resident Attendants". William Fry was appointed as Horseman "at the wage of 24/- weekly", the cart horse being purchased from the Birmingham Corporation.

Both the male and female members of staff were required to wear uniform. The male members of staff were "provided with one uniform per annum, and when they work upon the land with a pair of leggings".

The Matron, Miss Carse commented upon the staff in her first annual report:

"Of the staff generally I cannot speak too highly; of course non (sic) are perfect, but they have never failed to accord me their loyal support in anything I have wished to attempt. The medical officer, assistant matron, farm bailiff and myself have worked most happily together, and I feel it is to the general staff that the thanks of the Committee are due for anything that has been achieved. With less loyal people around me it would have been impossible to attempt what has been done."

The Life of the Colonists

The first colonists, as they were then called, were received on April 23rd 1908. Unfortunately, no records now remain of the names of these men and women. They are referred to in terms of numbers and classification only. The first annual report of the Matron records the monthly admissions for the first year as being:

April	1908	63	October	1908	1
May	"	66	November	"	6
June	"	1	December	"	2
July	"	19	January	1909	1
August	"	25	February	"	3
September	"	8	March	"	1

Group of female colonists 1913

"making the total number of admissions to the end of the year 196, of which number 6 died, 30 returned to their Unions, 1 discharged through King's Norton Union, leaving 159 in residence at the end of March." Of these, 70 were men (42 classed as epileptic and 28 as feebleminded), and 89 were women (39 classed as epileptic and 50 as feebleminded). By 1911 there were 111 men, 134, women and 7 children (being temporarily accommodated), a total of 252 colonists of which 112 were classed as epileptic and 140 as feebleminded.

At first, the Committee had to turn down applications from other Unions for the admission of patients, until they had had 12 months experience in running the colony. Those deemed "unsuitable for Colony treatment" were gradually returned to their respective institutions, i.e. the workhouses where they had previously been. The demand for places at Monyhull however, continued to grow.

Life at the colony was incredibly hard for those that lived there. The men and women were not only segregated from the wider community, but were also strictly segregated from each other inside the colony. Women were seen to be particularly vulnerable and those

Single storey home for men 1913

Two storey home for men 1913

who conceived children "out of wedlock" were rejected and banished from society (Blennerhassett 1995). Added to this were the fears that the nation would degenerate if the "feebleminded" had children freely. Segregation and enforced sterilisation had therefore become an accepted means of social control. Dr. Jordan, the medical officer advocated the value of segregation, believing it to be "the main beneficial result to be obtained from the formation of Colonies". He also credited the policy of segregation as being the explanation for the "relatively greater improvement of our female colonists". His views therefore reflect the attitudes and social mores of the time:

"Women bear segregation, by virtue of inherent and unalterable laws of human nature, much better than do men. When the epileptic and feebleminded young woman is removed to an institution from outside temptations, to which by reason of her special defects she is very liable to fall a victim, she soon ceases to be tempted; becomes more quickly serene in mind, takes more kindly to regular and directed work; and therefore derives a more full advantage from the surroundings which are favourable to her progress. On the other hand, the feebleminded man, and especially the male sane epileptic, is prone, for some time at least, to dislike segregation, to desire his personal freedom at the expense of his well-being; and so some of the male epileptics, though I am glad to say in a lessening degree, are more difficult to manage than the female epileptics."

Discipline was also advocated as a means of control. The role of the nurses and attendants was mainly custodial and based on maintaining order. The colonists were seen to be people who needed to be "managed" and "more easily influenced by and amenable to the nursing staff." Dr. Jordan believed in the "value of essential but mild discipline". One disciplinary measure was to order a "sufficient but less generous dietary (sic)." Another was to refuse leave of absence, which was granted as a "reward for good conduct."

"My medical treatment would have been less effectual had not the necessary discipline been insisted upon. This discipline, mild in its character, and firmly, but kindly enforced by Matron, forms an inherent part of the successful management of the colonists by the staff. Our colonists, from the nature of their affliction, stand in more need of personal control and supervision than does the average normal person. All good and successful

men and women have been disciplined in their youth, and continue to discipline themselves. Our colonists cannot discipline themselves, but they can learn to obey our few and simple rules, and by doing so, can become, as most of them have become, good, happy and successful colonists."

All of the colonists were set to work in some area or another, although they received no wages for the work that they did. It has to be remembered that Monyhull was established as an "Industrial Colony", with the aim that "each colonist shall become an active factor in the community of the Colony by receiving instruction and performing duties suitable to his or her age and capacity." Initially the men were engaged on various sections of farmwork, including "the lawns and greenhouses, the orchard and kitchen garden, the cowsheds and yard, with the carpenter, with the bricklayer, with the painters, with the hedger, on the grounds around the homes, on the farm and wood chopping". Others were employed in the stores, in the cooking kitchen yard, as gate-openers, and as stokers.

Matron reported after the first year that;

"the majority of these men had no idea of work beyond a little scrubbing, dusting or brass-polishing, so they had to be 'broken' in to it. There has been a good deal of time and patience expended on them, and it has been no easy task to get even a small amount of good work done by them. However, they have improved - some of them considerably - and the market value of their work is greater today than twelve months ago, and I hope will go on increasing. What I feel should be aimed at is some employment for all. The worst feebleminded men wheel barrows, sweep up, pick up stones, and such-like odd jobs, and they work the same number of hours as the others, that is, from 8a.m. to 1p.m., with fifteen minutes for lunch, and from 1-15p.m. to 5p.m. Some work longer than this, and, as these are the best workers, they are proud to do it. It is a very rare thing now to hear of a man refusing to work. At first this was one of our greatest difficulties."

William Fife, the farm bailiff, also reported on the work of the colonists after the first year:

"During the first few weeks I often felt downhearted when I looked on the work being done, and felt as if our labour was all in vain; but gradually, as the Colonists began to learn how to handle tools, the prospects got brighter, and the improvement has been maintained throughout the year. The Colonists were raw to the work, but soon began to see what was required, and how to do it, and from that time things seemed to change, the work went on much better, the men got a much healthier appearance, were more able to do the work, and did it in a much better way. More men can now be worked with one attendant, but it is most difficult to estimate how many Colonists would be required to do one man's work, as the nature of our work has varied so much, and they have to be taught new things regularly. In some sorts of work two men will do a man's work; in others, six would not do it; but time will improve them."

The women colonists were employed in the "Sewing Room, Laundry, General work in Homes etc., Housemaids' work etc., Cooking kitchen and scullery." Again, Matron reported on their progress:

"The work done in the sewing room commenced in July 1908, and from that date to the end of March upwards of 2,000 garments were made, comprising shirts, vests, night-shirts, chemises, night-gowns, petticoats, dresses etc., and also all the uniforms of nurses who have come since July. There have also been 53 pairs of socks and stockings knitted by hand. This does not exhaust the work done in the sewing room, as all repairs from the male homes are done there, except the sewing on of buttons, which is chiefly done by the young boys. Practically the whole of the women have been taught to both sew and knit since coming here, and although they considered it a hardship at first to be compelled to work a certain length of time or do a given amount, they appreciate it now, and take a greater interest in their work. As regards the laundry, here again is a marked improvement in the way the women do the work. The number of articles dealt with each week is upwards of 3,000, and now, the women do most of the actual work under supervision. Some of them are being taught finer ironing, and if one shows a special aptitude for a certain class of work she is encouraged in it, so long as her conduct is satisfactory. I am attempting to train some of the younger girls as housemaids and waiting maids. One or two are fairly promising, but so many bad habits have to be broken down that it is very uphill work for those immediately over them. Later I hope it will be found possible to have other employment for the women and girls; but this will come as a natural result of the development of the Colony."

Dr. Jordan, when reviewing the progress of the colony in 1912, wrote about "the value of work":

"Carefully organised and directed work has been the most valuable agent in bringing about the improvement of the colonists. The members of the Committee, have often witnessed the colonists at work, and have then seen how each one is employed on work suited to his or her capacity and strength. On the first visit, nearly all of you saw an exhibition of work which had been done and also some of them at work in the new and well equipped workshops then opened by the Chairman of the Committee. Frequently as I visit the Colony, I must frankly admit that the work I then saw was as astonishing to me as it was gratifying, and full of hope for the future. I knew that the work had been gradually improving; but until I saw that exhibition, I had no adequate conception of what had been accomplished by the joint efforts of an untiring and devoted staff and of willing and capable colonists."

"The true value of the work of the colonists is the educational effect it has on them as men and women. The constant aim of our training is to develop to the fullest extent every faculty of mind and body which can improve them in character and in capacity, and so make their lives more and more happy. Every one of the colonists is made the most of and it is astonishing how "much" that "most" is in the case of many of them."

At first, Monyhull was very much a closed community. Colonists were not allowed to leave the grounds unless they had been granted 'leave of absence' by the Matron, and then only "when satisfied that the Colonist will be under safe and proper control from the time of starting to return to the Colony" with a written undertaking. Leave was granted for good conduct and limited to one grant in three months. Walks outside the colony had to be in the company of "adequate attendants" and "to be taken mainly (but not entirely) along the unfrequented roads". Visiting Day was on "the first Saturday in every alternate month from 3 to 5p.m. in the summer and 2 to 4p.m in the winter." Visitors were only admitted if they had a Visiting Card issued by the Matron.

It was not all work and regulations however. The men played cricket and football, with matches arranged every Saturday afternoon and bank holidays. Teams consisted of both colonists and staff. The women had no outdoor games except "ball" and skipping, although they did have "simple drilling exercise". Evening classes for both men and women were provided in reading, writing, spelling and arithmetic, picture framing and fret work, fancy needlework and paper flower making. Saturday evenings were given over to "music, dancing and games in both the male and female Homes" before the assembly hall was built, which then became the venue for dances and concerts. Both the staff and the colonists produced and gave concerts at Christmas time.

Outings were also enjoyed. On July 28th 1909:

"in commemoration of the late King Edward's visit to the city, the whole of the Colonists and nursing staff, numbering upwards of 200, were taken by barges on the canal to Salter's Street (Earlswood) where a field for games, and the schoolroom in which to have tea, were placed at our disposal. The outing was enjoyed by all. Many of the Colonists had not been on the water before, and as the weather was fine, they considered it a most perfect holiday, although it was described by one of the young Colonists when writing to his father, as "a trip in coal-boats up the cut !"

The Farms and Estates

The colony was to be mainly self supporting, thanks to the work of the colonists and the two farms, Bells Farm and Kingswood, which formed part of the estate. Bells Farm was the residence of the farm bailiff. The house itself was built in the 17th century, and had close links with the manor of Monyhull even then. It had a secret staircase in one of its walls and a tunnel, which were probably used as a hiding place in the time of religious persecution following the Gunpowder Plot of 1605. When William Fife took over residency on the 25th May 1908, he had an enormous task ahead of him:

"Only a partial report can be given as yet regarding the farm, seeing that the pasture land has only been occupied since Michaelmas last, except one field of six acres, on which potatoes were grown last season. The crop of potatoes was very satisfactory, when it is taken into consideration that the land was old pasture, and only ploughed up in the spring of 1908, and the seed dibbled

Bells Farmhouse, home of the Farm Bailiff.

into the furrows. The potatoes were all consumed on the Colony, and there was sufficient for the requirements of the place until near the end of April. The same field is again planted with potatoes, and being in very good condition, ought to produce a good crop. This year another lea field of 10 acres has been broken up, between the laundry and the canal, for the cultivation this season of mangolds, swedes, cabbages etc. The land under cultivation seems to be good loam, and should prove suitable for the necessary crops of vegetables etc. for use on the Colony."

"Since the 1st of last October all the milk consumed on the Colony has been produced by our own cows, which have passed the test for tuberculosis....The total live stock includes:- 2 farm horses, 2 ponies and 1 small pony, 6 cows, 19 heifers, 3 calves, 1 bull, 37 sheep, and 13 pigs. The poultry number about 100 hens and 100 chickens."

"The digging of the orchard has been entirely done by three unemployed men, who have been of very great assistance in doing a good amount of work which we would not have been able to get through in time to get the orchard cropped this season. In the old pool below the orchard 500 osiers have been planted. Near No. 3 Home a piece of ground has been trenched and planted with 475 roots of rhubarb. Vegetables of various kinds are also being grown in the kitchen garden, and on the new piece which has been taken in on the southwest side of the garden wall. Kidney beans have been planted on the piece of land behind No. 5 and No. 6 Homes."

The first year of the colony also saw much in the way of building and repair work:

"All the ivy has been cleared from the roofs of the buildings and from under the eaves. The removing of the ivy from amongst the tiles necessitated the repairing of the roofs and the rebuilding of the greater part of the gables, as the roots seemed to be everywhere. The walls of the clock tower were strengthened with four brick pillars inside, and the top of the tower, owing to decay, had to be taken down and a new one put on. The clock was thoroughly repaired and overhauled, and is now in good working order. The piggery walls were entirely pulled down and rebuilt. A new concrete floor was put in, after raising the bottom about 2 feet. The old closets were pulled down and rebuilt, and a urinal has since been built in the same place. New coal houses have been built at the Gardener's Cottage and at the Old Lodge, and at the latter the closet has been altered, the chimney pulled down and rebuilt, and better ventilation put into the bedroom. Two iron buildings, 70ft. by 30ft. were purchased and erected by contract. One is being used for wood cutting, and for keeping tools, barrows etc. and is a most useful building; while the other, which is fitted up for an assembly room, is very useful for this purpose."

Plans for Expansion

The demand for places at Monyhull continued to grow. A "census" of 1910 obtained by the Joint Committee found that 850 "mentally defective" people were chargeable to the combined boards, and that "upwards of 200 of that number...were suitable for treatment in the Colony". Now that the colony "no longer had the uncertainty of pioneering but could properly be regarded as a proved success", the Joint Committee were able to approve an extension scheme. It was planned that the colony would be extended to :

Female Side: Two two-storey Homes, each accommodating 42.
Four single-storey Homes, each accommodating 42.

Male Side: Two two-storey Homes, each accommodating 42.
Four single-storey Homes, each accommodating 42.

Monyhull Cottage, staff residence 1913.

Line drawing of the Assembly Hall.

Administration Block, with accommodation for 40 Officers.
The Old Hall, with accommodation for 10 Officers.
Monyhull Cottage, with accommodation for 10 Officers.
Chapel, with sittings for 500 persons.
Assembly Hall, to accommodate 500 persons.
Bakehouse.
Boilerhouse for supplying steam to the kitchen.
Kitchen Block.
Dairy.
Laundry.
Workshops.
Stables and Farm Buildings.

It was also decided to include provision for children in the extension scheme. Children had been excluded from the plans for the first instalment of the colony, as it had been assumed that the Birmingham City Education Committee would provide accommodation for mentally defective children, including those chargeable to the Joint Committee. However, negotiations reopened in October 1909, at the request of the Education Committee, and it was agreed that "as the Joint Poor Law Committee already possessed a site and the chief administrative staff, it would be advantageous and economical if they could provide accommodation at the Colony for the mentally defective children chargeable to the Guardians and also for suitable cases from the City Education Committee."

On 4th June 1912, the City Council requested that "subject to the approval of the Board of Education, the Birmingham Board of Guardians be asked to provide at Monyhull Colony residential School accommodation for 50 epileptic and 180 mentally defective children to be sent there by the Education Committee." By 19th June the request had been accepted, with additional plans to provide accommodation for 115 Poor Law children, bringing the total up to 345. The joint scheme between the Guardians and the City Council was embodied in an agreement on 28th February 1913, and approved by the Local Government Board and the Board of Education. It was the first agreement of its kind and the principal points are as follows:

(1) The Guardians to provide at Monyhull Colony accommodation for the reception, maintenance, and education of epileptic and feebleminded children (hereinafter referred to as "City children").

(2) The accommodation to be provided to comprise detached or semi-detached houses, school buildings, workshops, officers' residential quarters, and all the necessary equipment of a school certified under the Elementary Education (Defective and Epileptic Children) Act, 1899.

(3) The Education Authority to undertake to contribute in the manner hereinafter indicated in respect of 230 children, or such further number as may be hereafter agreed.

(4) Both parties at all times to use their best endeavours to obtain and maintain in respect of the school a certificate of the Board of Education under the Elementary Education (Defective and Epileptic Children) Act, 1899, or any amending Act.

It was planned that the children's section would consist of:

Female Side:	One Home accommodating 38 epileptics.
	Three Homes, each accommodating 45 feebleminded.
Male Side:	One Home accommodating 38 epileptics.
	Three Homes, each accommodating 45 feebleminded.

Receiving Home, 20 beds.
School with 300 places, including separate class rooms for epileptics.
Hand Laundry for girls.
Workshops for boys.

The contract for the extensions was entered into in February 1913, and work commenced shortly afterwards. However, before the work had been completed, the country found itself at war.

Chapter 3

The Mental Deficiency Act 1913

The report of Lord Radnor's Royal Commission on the Care and Control of the Feebleminded led to the passing of the Mental Deficiency Act of 1913; "an Act to make further and better provision for the care of the feebleminded and other mentally defective persons and to amend the Lunacy Acts." The Act adopted the Royal Commission's definition of "mental deficiency", with four subdivisions of "idiocy", "imbecility", "moral imbecility" and "feeblemindedness". This was based on the advice of the medical organisations, and finally drew a line between mental deficiency and mental illness. It also gave wider powers to authorities to remove people from the community and place them under guardianship or into institutions. People could now be certified if in addition to being a "defective" that person was abandoned, neglected or without visible means of support; guilty of any criminal offence; undergoing imprisonment or detention in a reformatory, industrial school, inebriate reformatory or an institution for "lunatics"; a habitual drunkard within the Inebriates Acts 1879 to 1900; or in receipt of poor relief at the time of giving birth to an illegitimate child. People classed as "idiots" or "imbeciles" were to be certified by two qualified medical practitioners, one of whom was to be approved by the local authority. Those classed as "feebleminded" also had their certificates signed by a judicial authority. The authorities were to review these orders after twelve months and then for successive periods of five years. Parents or guardians could write to the authority if they wanted to remove their charge from the institution. The authority then had a legal obligation to "consider the care and supervision available if discharged and decide within 14 days if further detention is required in the interests of the defective." Once inside the institutions however, it was usually difficult to get out, at least legally. Many absconded, only to be brought back if "caught".

Monyhull Colony, of course, was already well established at the time of the Act, and was approved by the Board of Control as a Certified Institution on the 13th May 1914. The Board of Guardians immediately entered into an agreement with Birmingham City Council to admit those people who now came under the Act, and for whom the Council were responsible. A similar provision was later made with Smethwick County Borough Council.

Mr. R. J. Curtis, Clerk to the Board, discussed the progress being made at Monyhull in a paper presented at the Poor Law Conferences of 1913-14 in response to the Mental Deficiency Act. He urged the other authorities to follow Monyhull's lead in accordance with the new act. In the discussion that followed, Birmingham was congratulated upon its "foresight in founding the Monyhull Colony" and delegates agreed that the "Monyhull experience had been invaluable". Visitors to the colony expressed their "admiration of the enterprising and humanitarian spirit which has brought the colony into existence and which has done so much to ameliorate the lot of an unfortunate class of the community." Others commented that it was a "lead which must be followed all over the country in the best interests of the nation and the race." Those in positions of authority agreed that these "unfortunate citizens", as they had been deemed, should be provided for in special institutions.

While authorities around the country were considering the implications of the new act, the extension scheme at Monyhull was well underway. It was formally inaugurated by the laying of the foundation stone at the residential school on 14th November 1913, by the Home Secretary, The Right Hon. R. McKenna, M.P.

Then, in August 1914, Britain declared war on Germany.

A Military Hospital

The extensions to the adult section were sufficiently completed before the outbreak of war, to allow the new admissions to be accommodated, but the children's section had not yet been completed,

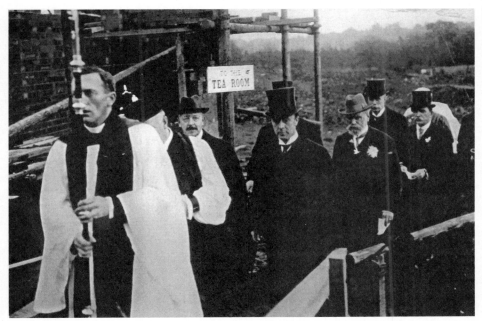

Foundation stonelaying by the Right Hon. Reginald McKenna MP (Secretary of State for Home Affairs) November 14th 1913.

when in January 1916, the Army Council asked to be able to use it as a military hospital. A total of 125,031 men were brought to Birmingham for treatment during the war, and special hospital facilities were set up for them at Birmingham University, the Poor Law Infirmary in Dudley Road, Wordsley Workhouse Infirmary near Stourbridge, and even in elementary school buildings in Kings Heath and Stirchley (Lethbridge 1993). In 1916 then, Monyhull joined the list to become a 400 bed military hospital.

Some 5,000 patients were treated at Monyhull between 1916 and 1919. Convoys of wounded soldiers, including many colonial troops arrived almost daily. "One section of the hospital was especially set aside for the nursing of the many severe shell-shock cases that were brought here" (Rogers 1972).

Monyhull also began to admit "Service Patients", these being "epileptic discharged soldiers", who had been sent to the Colony by the local war pensions committees. The first such patient was admitted in

March 1917, and Matron reported that:

"he had lost his voice on admission as the result of a fit, but from the first he grumbled, was discontented and did not intend to stay; he was kept in bed for three days for observation; he was put into a small dormitory, had a fire there, an armchair for when he was up, and was made as comfortable as possible; his meals were served specially in every way, yet he was not contented, and absconded on the 23rd inst. He had only been five months in the Army, had seen no fighting, but, of course, constantly said that 'this was all he got after having served his King and Country'."

It must have been incredibly difficult for the ex-service men to adjust to life at Monyhull. A list of rules was set out for them, although Matron commented that "it is not desirable that too many restrictions should be placed upon the men, so as to make it too much like an Institution to them, or it may become irksome and irritate them":

---

1. All Service Patients must turn out to work at the hours given in rules.
2. All Service Patients must decide upon admission to the Colony, what kind of outdoor work they desire to learn during their twelve months residence, whether farm work or gardening, and they are to obey the Farm Bailiff's rules as to the hours of work, and his orders during those hours. If there is any special branch of work which they desire to learn, they must apply to the Matron, when arrangements will be made, as far as possible to meet their wishes.
3. No Service Patient is to leave the Colony without a Pass, or alone, and is to return not later than the time stated thereon.
4. The following hours must be kept:-

Weekdays

	Milkers		Non-milkers
Rise	5.45 a.m.	Rise	6.30 a.m.
Cowsheds	6.30 "	Breakfast	7.30 "
Breakfast	8.00 "	Work	8.00 "
Work	9.00 "	Dinner	12.30 p.m.
Dinner	12.30 p.m.	Tea	5.30 "

Tea	5.30 "	Supper	9.00 "
Supper	9.00 "	Lights-out	10.00 "
Lights-out	10.00 "		

Sundays

Farm Bailiff's hours.	Rise	7.00 a.m.
Milkers are to do this	Breakfast	8.00 "
work morning and evening,	Dinner	12.30 p.m.
also on weekends,as arranged	Tea	5.00 "
by the Farm Bailiff.	Supper	9.00 "
	Lights-out	10.00 "

5. All Service Patients must clean their own boots, and brush their own clothes, and when in the Home, help in keeping it clean and tidy; they must not expectorate about the rooms or corridors, nor over the fireplaces.

6. In the event of any Service Patient desiring, for any reason, to pay a visit to friends at a distance, at least 48 hours notice must be given to the Matron, together with the name and address of the people who wish him to visit them, so that a communication may be sent, giving the time of arrival, etc. and he must pay his own fare, or his friends must send the money. No leave of absence can be granted during work-hours.

Nevertheless, some of the Service Patients did try to make Monyhull their home for a short while. They named Home 9, where they resided, the "Homestead" and even wrote the following letter to the Matron to try to make their lives a little easier:

"The Homestead"
Monyhull Colony

To the Matron
Monyhull Colony,
Kings Heath,

Matron,
   The Service Patients of "The Homestead" wish to put forward the following propositions and hope that you will see your way to agree with them.

No. 1 Now that the light nights are coming on we wish to propose that a Pass should be granted to each of the patients in the middle of the week, say on Wednesday evening from 5.30 p.m. to 9p.m. independent of the Passes granted on Saturday and Sunday.

No. 2 That brass staples should be fixed on the locker of each patient so that he should be able to lock up his private belongings or that locks should be fixed to each locker.

No. 3 As there are many patients who would like to go into Birmingham each week, and find it almost impossible to bear the expenses of travelling in the tram, would it be possible for the Committee to grant a free tram pass to each of the patients.

No. 4 That the patients should be granted 6 or 7 days leave every three months, and that either a free railway warrant or a half fare voucher should be granted so that each patient should be able to proceed to his home.
Would you please write to the Ministry of Pensions with regard to the travelling warrants and vouchers?

Thanking you in anticipation,
                                   we remain,
                                             Yours obediently,

However, the reports constantly refer to "troublesome" Service Patients. On September 25th 1918, it was reported:

"We now have twenty six Service Patients in the "Homestead", three have been returned to their homes this week, one....as he is quite unsuitable, and is very dirty in his habits and too mental to remain here;...one...has been a constant source of trouble since he came, and on Saturday night came in drunk; he was insolent to the Attendant, walked into the Observation room, took a loaf of bread off Mr. Bank's table, and when remonstrated with, he emptied a jug of coffee over him, spoiling his overcoat. The other man... has been getting more insolent, and he gambles a great deal and encourages the others to do so."

It seems that quite a few of the Service Patients had to be transferred or discharged on account of their behaviour. On June 4th 1919, a deputation was sent from the War Pensions Committee of Mansfield in response to complaints made by some of the men who had left the colony. On June 17th, the Committee wrote back to the Matron, saying "after hearing their report my Committee instructed me to inform you that they are of the opinion that your Institution is in every respect suitable for the treatment of Epileptic discharged soldiers, ...and they will not hesitate to send other patients to your Institution." The Service Patients were finally discharged or sent to Hollymoor Hospital in July 1920. The "Homestead" became another home for the colonists.

Of course the war was at an end by this time. Armistice Day (November 1918) was celebrated at Monyhull like everywhere else:

"As soon as the maroons (sic) sounded the Colonists were got together and flags given out to them when assembled at the top of the drive, where they sang the Doxology and a verse of the National Anthem, afterwards marching round the Colony with the flags, which were eventually fixed up in different parts of the buildings and on the trees. The Colonists were granted the remainder of the day as holiday and a great number were taken out on road walks, some of the women and children being taken into Kings Heath to see the decorations. The following Wednesday a Thanksgiving Service was held in our own Church, conducted by the Chaplain, the Rev. Hugh Price, and practically the whole of the Colonists attended this and took great interest in it. All the Staff had special time off duty that week, so that as far as possible everyone participated in the general thanksgiving and rejoicing for the first part of the Peace proclamation."

The Army Council vacated the buildings in the children's section on the 31st December 1919. The buildings then had to be restored before they could be used for the children. The Guardians finally completed their extension scheme in 1920.

Monyhull During the War Years

Between 1914 and 1918, the number of colonists (men, women and children) rose to around 650. A Local Government Inspector, visiting the colony in 1916 "appeared satisfied with all he saw, but made some remarks about the overcrowding and the impossibility of classification of Colonists under present conditions." There was nothing that could be done however. Monyhull had to admit those people who now came under the Mental Deficiency Act, as well as taking in patients from other infirmaries to make room for wounded soldiers. Overcrowding, however, was not the only serious problem endured during the war. Food rationing was causing even greater distress, resulting in drastic weight loss and sickness. In February 1917, Matron was compelled to report the situation in detail to the Board:

"As regards the Food Controller's allowance of bread, I am afraid it will cause a very great hardship to the Colonists if we are compelled to cut down their allowance to 9 ozs a day, as they are all very big bread eaters, and have been accustomed to have bread and cheese for lunch when out on the Land, and as they are some distance from their homes, it is impossible to substitute anything for this...It is much more difficult here than in a family, or Institution where there are a number of children or sick people; both as regards Officers and Colonists, we are all adults...2 1/2 lbs. of Meat per week, including every kind of Meat and Fish, is a very small amount to be divided into seven days, and substitutes are difficult to get. I am doing my best to cut down the food, but hesitate to go too far so as to cause ill health amongst resident Officers on the Staff, which is already depleted, without having anyone off duty sick."

Two months later, the situation had got worse:

"We have had more sickness during this last month than we have had for some time previously; I am afraid it must be put down, to a very great extent, to the restricted dietary (sic). There are at the present time about thirty four men in the Male Homes who are undoubtedly suffering from lack of nourishment, which can only be supplied by bread,

Nursing staff outside Monyhull Hall, 1914.

Matron Carse and nursing staff 1914.

but if I am to keep to anything like the 4 lbs. allowed by the Food Controller, it is impossible for me to give more, although I am told my issue is the highest throughout the Union...I have been obliged to increase the allowance to the children, because upon them being weighed in the month of March, it was found that the majority of them had lost from 2 to 4 lbs."

"It is very difficult where you are not making bread, to make full use of the substitutes given. For instance you are to use oatmeal, sago, rice, barley, tapioca and margarine. At the present time, and for some weeks now, a second pudding has been given every day to make up for no bread being given at Dinner time; oatmeal porridge is given three mornings in the week. These people cannot stand more oatmeal than this, without their skin getting into an inflamed condition...We are not getting our full supply of fresh milk, which is necessary to make milk puddings to give the full amount of nutrition...also we are practically getting no fresh vegetables, upon which these people have always done so well...the amount of sugar has been cut down, which hitherto has helped to give a certain amount of heat, which epileptics require, because of their poor circulation."

"I feel responsible for the helpless people who are placed here in the care of whoever happens to be the head of the Institution. It is a totally different matter from them going into a "house" from which they can take their discharge at any moment if they are not satisfied...the Colonists here cannot do anything, except steal to get more nutrition or more food, and are therefore quite at our mercy."

To add to the misery, an influenza pandemic had broken out, killing 40 million people worldwide; 250,000 in Britain. Monyhull was badly affected. Inevitably, with so many people living in close proximity to one another, the epidemic spread quickly. November 1918 saw "the worst epidemic of sickness that has been experienced since the Colony was opened almost eleven years ago." There were 420 cases of influenza, "having at one time 359 in bed", and six deaths. There were also 21 cases amongst the staff. Matron praised the efforts of staff members: "I cannot speak too highly of the way in which the Assistant Matrons, Nurses and Attendants carried out their very trying duties during this epidemic."

There was some cause for celebration during these difficult times however. The chapel was opened on the 30th June 1917, by Canon Astbury (Chairman of the Monyhull Colony Committee). Dr. Wakefield, the Bishop of Birmingham, Canon Price, the Chaplain, and the Rev. Jones, who represented the Birmingham Evangelical Free Church also attended. C. Rogers, organist at the church from 1918 to 1965, remembered the ceremony:

> *"Canon Price arranged an excellent service to mark this great occasion and the organist and choir of the Parish Church officiated too. As a chorister I was present at this service, and I can recall Canon Astbury performing the opening ceremony with a silver key, followed by the impressive service afterwards, and an excellent strawberry tea provided by Matron Carse in the Assembly Hall when the service was over."*

Matron herself reported:

> *"we fully appreciate having a building set apart for religious services; personally, I am very proud of it, and feel that the decision of the Committee to erect such a building, was one of the chief things towards helping forward the work of the Colony and endeavouring to place it on a higher level."*

The chapel was later to be dedicated to St. Francis of Assisi.

The Monyhull Children

The 1913 Mental Deficiency Act stated that the local education authorities had to give the Board of Control notice of all children over the age of 7 who were certified as being defective. Under the Act, any child who was deemed "incapable by reason of mental defect of receiving benefit or further benefit in special schools or classes, or who cannot be instructed in a special school or class without detriment to the interests of the other children" was to be placed under guardianship or sent to an institution.

The children who were received at Monyhull, however, were not considered to be "ineducable". Before the purpose built school was completed, the children received regular lessons in the assembly hall. In 1917 there were some 80 children at Monyhull, and they attended lessons provided by the teacher Miss Treen and her assistant. The Board of Control also offered to train a teacher for them, "a girl to have handled a class and to know a little of school methods and routine. The ideal

Group of children housed at the colony 1913.

would be an Infant School Teacher of about 25 years who is fond of children and has a natural gift for teaching. Failing this a Nurse Attendant who would like to specialise in School Work."

The residential school, which became known as St. Francis School (and later Lindsworth), was opened in 1920, for every child in the colony for training up to the age of 16 years, "unless excluded by the Medical Officer for special reasons." Its objective was to provide general education until the age of 12 or 13, and then to gradually concentrate on specialised work or training. Every child was examined on admission to the school and at frequent periods during the school year, with particular importance "paid to the provision of the individual's powers and needs." The school consisted of the following sections:

The Lower School: Class 1. Nursery Class
                       Class 2. Preparatory or Test Class

The Upper School: Class 3. Three R. Class - Division A

Class 4. Three R. Class - Division B
Class 5. Junior Boys Handicraft Class
Class 6. Three R. Class - Division C
Class 7. Three R. Class - Division D
Housewifery and Needlework Training Centre: Lower Division
Upper Division

School Workshops: Senior Boys' Handicraft
Shoemaking Instruction

The Committee described the division of the classes and the education provided:

"The Nursery Class is comprised of children of varying ages of the lowest grades of mentality. The Preparatory or Testing Class is comprised of children chiefly of the younger trainable low grade section, and is also a special testing class for young children who, on admission, do not reveal themselves when first examined sufficiently to determine whether suitable for the lower Three R Division. The lowest Housewifery and Handicraft Section comprises the older trainable low grade children. The aim in this

Children ready for concert 1913.

class is to provide a type of special handwork training that even if on mechanical lines will enable the children to take some useful place as workers after school age."

The school curriculum consisted of religious instruction, physical training, reading, writing, and number training, general handiwork training, preliminary industrial training, and workshop and workroom instruction.

Initially, there were eight teachers in the upper school along with the Headmistress, with two members of staff having "large experience in teaching mentally defective children" and holding a teaching certificate. The remaining teachers were to receive training by attending other institutions for a few weeks. The Inspectors reported that:

"the school is organised and conducted successfully by Miss Redfern who possesses the unusual gifts of lively intelligence, foresight and skill for the work. She has had many years experience in the work which she uses to good purpose at every point. The small classes have given the teachers a great chance of giving individual attention to the children and judging from the excellent manual work which I saw, the teachers have made full use of this opportunity."

By 1926 there were over 300 children living at Monyhull. Outside of school they put on their own concerts in the assembly hall, and played games and sports. Picnics were also held in the summer when the weather was fine, with outdoor games and "special teas" provided for them.

Few accounts of life as a child at Monyhull have been recorded. Raymond Jordan, who was admitted to the children's section at the age of 14, lived at Monyhull for 40 years. Confined to a wheelchair, with very little use in his arms and legs, and with no speech, he learned to use an electric typewriter by means of an attachment to his foot. His "courage and unfailing sense of humour in the face of cruel physical disabilities" (Hull 1976) and his ability to overcome the obstacles to write his life story, were recognised by the Spastics Society Special Achievement Award in 1975. His memories of childhood at the colony are heart rending:

"No-one was allowed to go out of the Colony. It was a very strict place and life was hard. We were not allowed to have any contact with the female side. If anybody was caught talking to the girls they were put to bed or sent to Rampton, which was a kind of prison where you were kept under lock and key."

"When I first went to Monyhull I was on the Children's Side. I got on well with most of the other boys but there was one lad who was bigger and older than the rest of us who was nothing but a great big bully. He made you do what he told you to do and if you didn't obey him he would get some of the older boys to put a lump of soap in your mouth and tie a towel round your face and give you a good hiding. He made us save our food for his mates at school. We were too scared to say anything about it and we had to put up with this for years before he was found out and transferred to another home and peace of mind came to our home at last."

"During these years on the Children's Side life was very hard. There was always plenty of work for us to do. We had to get down on our hands and knees and scrub the floors or wash down the walls. We were just cheap labour, having to do any jobs that were given to us."

"We all looked forward to Sports Day and Christmas Day when we had a special treat. We really had a good time on Sports Day. All the homes would compete for cups and shields. We would also play football and cricket at weekends."

Many of the children who went to the school transferred to the adult section when they reached 16. Harold Hands first went to the colony in February 1926. He remained at Monyhull for 56 years, finally leaving at the age of 73. His memories describe what life was like for him:

"When I first went to Monyhull Colony it was on Monday, February the 8th, 1926. I remember it quite well. My mother took me there through epilepsy caused through meningitis of the brain when I was seven months old. I was blind for two years with it, I heard my mother say. When I reached the age of seven years I had my first fit. They used to send for my mother several times when I was at school and they asked her to have me put away which she did when I was turned fifteen years of age."

*Harold Hands, resident at Monyhull from 1926-1982
(with kind permission from Mrs Chapman, his sister).*

"When I first entered Monyhull Colony as it was then called I went in B2 on the Children's Section. I had to see the Medical Superintendent before I could go to school which is now St. Francis, but I was pleased to leave at 16 years of age. I went on the Men's Section in October of the same year. It wasn't too good then. We were made to pull a big roller round the field from 8.30 in the morning till 10 am. being lunch time and after lunch carry on till dinner time and we didn't get pocket money then like we do now."

"When I got to the age of 19 I was sent out to work on the land. We used to hoe in between the mangolds, kale and swedes up on Kingswood farm with an officer named Mr. X. He wasn't very nice to the patients. We used to be escorted to and from work six days a week. It wasn't very pleasant nor (sic) he wasn't. He used to make the patients work in the rain and we didn't have an overcoat, the staff in charge of the Home said we wasn't allowed them."

"On Sundays we were escorted to and from Church and if one of us got out of line we had a thick ear. What I am telling here is the truth. If you wished the staff good morning they used to get on a line and belt you for it. We used to have to be in bed at 7.30 pm. at night and up at 6.00 am. the next morning. It was awful. The food is a hundred per cent better now than it was then. We only had leave every three months and visiting day was the first Saturday in every two months."

It is only through recollections like these that we can understand what it was like to live in an institution.

Further Developments

The 1927 Mental Deficiency Amendment Act stated that the authorities should now also "provide suitable training or occupation for defectives who are under supervision or guardianship or have been sent to certified institutions." Monyhull had been doing this from the very beginning, and indeed, the question of increased workshop provision arose in 1921, when Matron reported that "the present shops are totally inadequate for our needs." She suggested that the present range of three shops could be adapted for the carpenters and their pupils, and also for increased storage room. It was also suggested that two large army huts be purchased, one to be used for shoemaking and the other for upholstering, "the latter to be erected near the Male Homes, which would be a much more convenient position as this work is supervised by the Head

The sewing room 1920.

The Haunch 1925
(with kind permission from Birmingham Central Library)

Attendant." The sewing rooms were also deemed to be overcrowded, making it difficult to deal with the increasing amount of work.

The new workshops were added, as well as other extensions to the colony in general. An X-ray department was established by Major Hall-Edwards, a British pioneer in X-ray treatment, when Monyhull was used as a military hospital during the war. There was also a mortuary, post-mortem and laboratory block, a single storey open air pavilion for the treatment of patients with tuberculosis, a treatment centre with electro-therapy department, dental room and dressing room, extra classrooms and extra stores. Electric lighting replaced the gas lamps. A "cinematography machine" was introduced to the assembly hall for entertainment.

During the first world war, the Committee bought "The Cottage", formally known as The Pleasaunce, on Monyhull Hall Road. It was purchased from the Aherne family, whose sons were both actors; Brian becoming a star in Hollywood. The Cottage became the residence of the Medical Superintendent. The Committee also acquired several large houses to provide further accommodation for "specially selected female patients". These were known as "The Haunch", "Trostrey", and "The Laurels". Two more homes were also erected on the site. The Monyhull estate had grown to over 320 acres.

Changes were also occurring on the medical and nursing side. In 1921, Miss M. J. Carse, Matron for some 14 years, retired due to ill health with the following tribute:

"The occasion of your retirement as Matron of Monyhull Colony affords the members of the Monyhull Colony Committee a fitting opportunity of recording their high appreciation of the invaluable services rendered by you for a period of 14 years. The Committee recall the fact that you were elected as the first Matron of the Colony in November 1907 and assisted to establish the Colony and begin the pioneer work of specialising in the treatment and training of the mentally deficient. The subsequent extensions to the Colony, their furnishing and equipment, the setting up of various training departments and the opening of the Residential School have emphasised the possession of administrative qualities of a high order which you have unsparingly given during a period of years rendered more difficult by the stress of a great war. The Committee much regret that through illhealth it has become necessary for you to relinquish the work to which you have so wholeheartedly devoted a large part of your life but which will be tempered by the satisfaction of knowing that you leave the Colony thoroughly organized and recognized all over the country as a model and up-to-date Institution. The members of the Committee and its officials who subscribe their names trust that with the relinquishment of your onerous duties you may have better health to enjoy your retirement."

She was replaced by Miss Cullwick, and the following year, Dr. A. McCutcheon, M.B., B.Ch., F.R.F.P.S. was appointed as the first Resident Medical Superintendent, "with special experience in psychological medicine." Monyhull became associated with the Joint Board of Mental Research established by the City and University of Birmingham and in 1927, became a recognized training school for nurses. Nurses were now to spend "two and a half years working with the patients and learning about mental deficiency, after which they took an examination to gain the certificate of the Royal Medico Psychological Association" (Kay 1976). The colony was also accepted for post graduate training for the Diploma in Psychological Medicine. Consultants and representatives from other authorities regularly visited the colony to study the work being done there.

Colonies were still seen to be the 'best solution' to the perceived social problems that people with learning disabilities caused. In 1929, this type of village colony "in which patients were housed in villas clustered around a central administrative block" was strongly advocated by the Mental Deficiency Committee (Alaszewski 1986). It was believed that "by this method proper classification in small units, varied trades and industries, economic maintenance, specialist medical attention, hospital facilities, adequate training of staff and opportunities for research can all be secured." The needs of the institution itself seemed to be taking over from the needs of the people who lived there; the very people for whom the institution had been established in the first place. The colonies were producing their own unique social problems. The effects of long term custodial care, of institutionalisation, were yet to be recognised.

Chapter 4

"On Licence"

The passing of the Local Government Act 1929 transferred the colony from the Poor Law Guardians to the Mental Deficiency Act Committee of the City Council. Twenty-three years of work under the Poor Law Acts had come to an end. In 1930, the Mental Treatment Act was passed , "to amend the Lunacy Acts of 1890 to 1922 and such of the provisions of the Mental Deficiency Acts 1913 to 1927 as relate to the Constitution and organisation of the work of the Board of Control, the exercise of the powers of the Board and the protection of persons putting those Acts into operation." Asylums were now to be called Mental Hospitals, "lunatics" to be termed "persons of unsound mind" and "paupers" to become "rate aided patients." The Act gave the authorities the power to receive voluntary patients and to provide

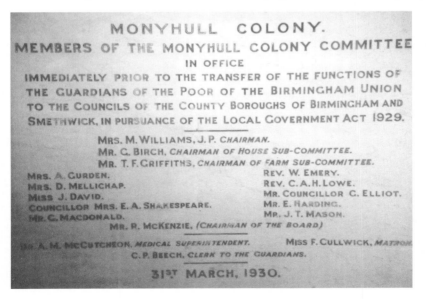

MONYHULL COLONY.

MEMBERS OF THE MONYHULL COLONY COMMITTEE
IN OFFICE
IMMEDIATELY PRIOR TO THE TRANSFER OF THE FUNCTIONS OF
THE GUARDIANS OF THE POOR OF THE BIRMINGHAM UNION
TO THE COUNCILS OF THE COUNTY BOROUGHS OF BIRMINGHAM AND
SMETHWICK, IN PURSUANCE OF THE LOCAL GOVERNMENT ACT 1929.

MRS. M. WILLIAMS, J. P. *CHAIRMAN.*
MR. G. BIRCH, *CHAIRMAN OF HOUSE SUB-COMMITTEE.*
MR. T. F. GRIFFITHS, *CHAIRMAN OF FARM SUB-COMMITTEE.*

MRS. A. CURDEN.
MRS. D. MELLICHAP.
MISS J. DAVID.
COUNCILLOR MRS. E. A. SHAKESPEARE.
MR. C. MACDONALD.

REV. W. EMERY.
REV. C. A. H. LOWE.
MR. COUNCILLOR G. ELLIOT.
MR. E. HARDING.
MR. J. T. MASON.

MR. R. MCKENZIE, *(CHAIRMAN OF THE BOARD)*

DR. A. M. McCUTCHEON, *MEDICAL SUPERINTENDENT.*   MISS F. CULLWICK, *MATRON.*
C. P. BEECH, *CLERK TO THE GUARDIANS.*

31ST MARCH, 1930.

Plaque to commemorate the passing of the colony to Birmingham City Council 31st March 1930.

Secretary of the Committee :

H.J. Clarke.

Telegrams :
"Avicenna, Parl., London."

THE BOARD OF CONTROL,

CAXTON HOUSE WEST,

TOTHILL STREET,

WESTMINSTER. S.W.1.

Departmental Committee on Mental Deficiency Colonies.

24th March, 1930.

Dear Dr. McCutcheon,

The Departmental Committee desire me to convey to you their grateful thanks for the time and trouble which you and members of your staff devoted to showing them over Monyhull Colony, and for your kind hospitality, when they visited last week.

They found their visit both interesting and instructive and have taken careful note of the views and information you were good enough to give them.

Yours very truly,

Secretary to the Committee.

A.M. McCutcheon, Esq., M.B., Ch.B.,
Monyhull Colony,
Birmingham.

Letter of thanks to Dr. McCutcheon from the Board of Control 1930.

temporary treatment without certification. The provisions of the Act however, mainly affected people with a mental illness rather than people with a learning disability. The terms "mental defective", "idiot", "imbecile" and "feebleminded" were retained, as was the term "colony."

The 1927 Mental Deficiency Act stressed that the duty of the authorities was to include supervision in the community as well as to provide occupation and training. It was the beginning of a change in attitude away from purely custodial care towards active rehabilitation and discharge. Straight out discharge was not the method approved by the Board of Control. Instead, they introduced a system of licensing, to care for "properly approved and suitable persons", who were to be "kept under careful supervision and helped in every way until such time as it may be possible to allow him to stand on his own feet." Any person on licence, with a view to discharge, remained under the control of the colony and could be "recalled" by the Medical Superintendent at any time. People could spend years on licence without being discharged.

The Board of Control, visiting Monyhull at the end of the 1920s, had commented on the "little use of Licence as a means of allowing patients to live outside the Colony and at the same time of ensuring the possibility of immediate recall." In 1931, only five patients were "on Licence." The Board of Control was concerned that "these small numbers of discharges and cases on licence indicate that the population of the Colony has to a large measure become a static one; and since the whole of the accommodation available is occupied, without increasing the accommodation but few cases can be admitted." This was indeed a problem as Monyhull was required by law to admit people certified under the Mental Deficiency Acts. The Committee accordingly aimed to "lead up to discharge to life outside wherever this can be safely and properly done." It was the duty of the medical superintendent, Dr. McCutcheon, to consider patients as to their suitability for a trial on licence from Monyhull. The Committee had already established ancillary homes for some patients, namely at The Haunch, Trostry, and the Laurels, but only a few of the patients, younger women "capable of doing useful work", were on licence. The

Board wanted the committee to develop a scheme for the transfer of "higher grade and more stable young patients to some satisfactory form of community care. Both in the interests of the patients themselves and those of the general economy." They also recommended the employment of a "Responsible Officer" to interview prospective employers in the community and to deal with the day to day problems of those in service. The situation slowly improved during the 1930s, with 86 patients on licence from Monyhull by 1937.

Life in an Institution

Despite these changes in attitudes, the number of people living in mental deficiency institutions across the country was rapidly rising, from 17,104 in 1924 to 51,214 in 1944 (Rooff 1957). The Manual for Mental Deficiency Nurses 1936 -37 was still advocating a custodial approach based on control. In many institutions, the Charge Nurse had become "a punitive authoritarian figure whose skill was equated in terms of maintaining order" (O'Hara 1967). The Medical Superintendent was seen to be "well nigh unapproachable...a remote being who offered a limp hand on Christmas morning" (ibid.), although this was the person who took decisions affecting everyone in the institution.

The custodial policy was still prevalent at Monyhull at this time. Although the colony was run on an "open door" system, this referred only to the boundaries of the colony, unless leave of absence had been granted or a person was on licence. It also only referred to the daytime. The Committee allowed people "to move as freely about their work and play as it is considered safe to permit, having regard to the Committee's legal and moral obligations." This meant however, that most people were always escorted by a member of staff. Difficulties arose from time to time, "as there are many dangerous and troublesome patients, but the bulk of them appreciate the conditions provided by the Committee, and try their best to fit in to the little community which a properly organized Colony should be." The "troublesome patients" were often those certified as being "moral defectives", who had been confined to an institution for socially unacceptable behaviour. When the number of people absconding from Monyhull began to increase, the Medical Superintendent "felt it necessary in the circumstances to lock the doors of some of the Homes which had hitherto been run on the open door principle."

The authorities controlled every aspect of life at the colony. In 1937 only the "higher grade" girls had been provided with their own individual clothes and bed linen with personal marking. The rest of the men and women had to wear the clothes that were given to them from the central store. One member of staff recalled how, as a young boy, he used to see the patients "dressed in dark grey Derby tweed suits, heavy duty boots and tweed cloth hats." The Inspectors recorded that they found the clothing to be more institutional than they were accustomed to seeing in other colonies; "almost all the women's overcoats were of the same pattern and colour and the coarse black stockings knitted in the colony might well be replaced by articles of lighter colour and texture" but that this should only be for "selected patients." Presumably, these "selected patients" were the ones who were allowed to work outside the colony. Hair cuts too, provided by members of staff, were functional, undifferentiated and often "grotesque in appearance."

There was no concept of individual choice as far as the colonists were concerned. Meals were cooked in the central kitchen and had to be delivered to each of the homes, often arriving cold, and with no "satisfactory apparatus" available for reheating them. Tea was provided in large tea-urns, with milk and sugar already added. On certain days, lard was "sent to the homes in place of margarine and spread on the patients' bread for breakfast and tea. This apparently results from the fact that margarine is not sent to the colony on those days." No-one had thought to change the ordering system.

Inspectors to the colony also commented that the provision of indoor entertainment was totally inadequate:

> *"there are no billiard or bagatelle tables nor any facilities for playing table tennis in any of the day rooms. The supply of playing cards, dominoes etc. is poor. It is difficult to believe that there are no occasions especially during the wintertime when patients would not be glad of such facilities."*

Men and women were still strictly segregated. It was "forbidden to go onto the female side from the male side" and vice versa. This applied to members of staff as well. A former male nurse recalled that it was "taboo to have anything to do with the female side...It was frowned upon to talk to the female patients." The suggestion of holding mixed dances at Monyhull was therefore a major step forward, although the focus still remained on maintaining strict control. The Board concluded that:

> *"whilst fully appreciating the inherent difficulties and dangers in an Institution of this kind, mixed dances have been found in other similar Institutions to serve a useful purpose provided that great care is exercised in the selection of patients to attend them. We cannot but feel sure that there are a number of suitable patients of both sexes in Monyhull who could safely attend dances of this kind, and who would properly appreciate them."*

The only other time patients (and staff) were allowed to mix freely was on the annual sports day. This was a huge event in which everyone at Monyhull was involved.

A poem written by Lily Miles, one of the women living in the hostels, captures the despair that must have been felt by many who had been certified and confined to life in an institution. Lily spent all of her adult life at Monyhull. She was admitted in 1915, at the age of 19 and died sixty-six years later.

From the Heart

The Monyhull walls are wide,
from end to end,
When I came here, I found no friend.

I left my home with an aching heart,
I had no-one to take my part.

While you lie sleeping,
I lie weeping, and
Many are the bitter tears I shed.
Although I am in this Colony and

hard is my lot,
I try to bear with content.
Oh dear friends, forget-me-not.

Lily Miles, Trostrey.

The Second World War

Life at Monyhull changed very little up to the second world war. The colony had become more overcrowded than ever, with 1307 people living there in 1940. Homes built for 40 people had to accommodate 50 or 60. Beds were squeezed into the dormitories. There was a shortage of staff, with many being called up for service in H.M. Forces. In some cases there would only be one member of staff to care for the needs of 60 people. The outbreak of the second world war meant that further recruitment and development were impossible. Plans to provide more hostels, particularly for male

Birmingham at war.
(photo by kind permission of Birmingham Central Library)

<u>M O N Y H U L L   C O L O N Y.</u>

<u>AIR RAID PROCEDURE AT NIGHT.</u>

<u>AT WARNING</u> –

1. PUT ON NOX LIGHT IN DORMITORY.

2. TAKE PATIENTS AS RAPIDLY AS POSSIBLE TO
   REFUGE ROOM.

3. TURN OUT ALL LIGHTS EXCEPT IN REFUGE ROOM.

4. IF ELECTRIC LIGHT FAILS IN REFUGE ROOM,
   LIGHT THE HURRICANE LAMPS.

<u>D O N'T</u> ALLOW GAS MASKS TO BE PUT ON UNLESS

<u>RATTLE</u> GIVES GAS WARNING.

A. M. McCUTCHEON,

<u>Medical Superintendent.</u>

<u>8th September, 1939.</u>

Monyhull Colony air raid procedure 1939.

patients who were on licence and yet still living at the colony had to be postponed. It was recognised that hostel development was essential to prepare patients for the community, and to allow training for paid employment.

Unlike the first world war, Monyhull was not scheduled to become a casualty hospital. The only facilities it was felt necessary to provide were those needed for treating minor injuries. The Medical Superintendent organised First Aid parties to deal with such an event. War time conditions were soon adapted to. Summer leave for the children was cancelled. A unit of the Local Defence Volunteer Force was formed by members of staff to patrol the colony. The Home Guard requisitioned a site at Bells Farm for the storage of explosives.

Scarcity of materials meant that less people could be employed in the workshops, and so many patients found themselves helping to dig out shelters in the grounds, or found work on the farms. In the event of daylight air raids, all patients were to cease work and be taken to the "appropriate refuge rooms."

Overcrowding was further complicated by air raid requirements:

"When there is an air raid the patients are crowded into the dormitory on the ground floor which is well protected by blast walls and wire netting on the inside of all windows. Except when an air raid is in progress the overcrowding does not appear to be more than that existing at most hospitals at present; probably the least satisfactory feature is the congestion in the day rooms, especially those occupied by the adults during the long winter evenings and on Sundays when weather conditions do not permit exercise out of doors."

The war years at Monyhull were again recorded by Raymond Jordan, a former resident:

"It was rather strange that it was during the war that our food and general conditions began to improve. We had more eggs and we got our regular rations so that there was more variety in our food. We had our own farm which helped us through and we never went short of food."

"One day we were playing football when four German planes swooped out of the sky with no warning. They went straight towards the Austin works. The warning was

given after they had gone over and we all went in until the all clear...In the early days of the war there were no air raid shelters for us. We had to get under the bed with only a pillow and the hard wooden floor. It was not very comfortable at all, very hard on the bones!...When the raids got very bad we slept in our dayroom, which had a thick outside wall built to stop the blast and paper stuck to the windows to stop splintering. We carried our mattresses and pillows down to the dayroom...Some nights the air raids were very bad. The staff did an ARP (Air Raid Patrol) rota at night and in one raid three male staff were killed by a bomb which dropped on the kitchen."

This air raid occurred on 28th November 1940. It was reported in the Birmingham Mail the following day:

Memorial tablet in memory of the men who lost their lives in an air raid on Monyhull 28th November 1940.

"There was a resumption last night of the air raids on the West Midland area, which for five nights has enjoyed a period of comparative quietude. None of the attacks was of an intensive nature and indeed for a considerable time they bore the character of 'nuisance' raids. They were, however, widespread."

"The raid was of long duration and in its course a large number of bombs, both of incendiary and explosive type, were dropped, but a high proportion of these fell in rural districts and caused small damage and few casualties."

"The most serious incident concerned a home for mental defectives where three sticks of bombs - nine in all - fell on buildings and in the grounds. There were three fatalities among the voluntary A.R.P. Workers of the institution, and a Sister was slightly cut."

"The fatalities comprised the 57 year old head warden, who was described by the Superintendent as one of the best men he had. He was standing at his post when the bomb fell but a few feet away from him. Another warden had gone out to chat with him, and he too lost his life. The third fatality was yet another warden who was just going on his patrol of the premises."

"The bomb that killed these men blasted windows in all directions, and put out of commission, temporarily at any rate, the main office. A reporter was told that one of the wardens was due to go out in the country with his wife and family today."

"Another bomb on the kitchen of the institution completely demolished its interior, while a further projectile struck the roof of the nurses home. There was no panic among any personnel or patients and some extremely good work was done by the female staff. One nurse earned the highest praise for the way in which she controlled and personally took charge of between 50 and 60 patients, although no assistance could be given to her for over an hour."

The men who lost their lives were Mr. Charles Davies, an attendant since 1930; Mr. William Turner, an attendant since 1915; and Mr. Frank Wood, a staff nurse since 1936. A memorial tablet was erected to their memory in the church at Monyhull. Their names continue to be read each Remembrance Sunday.

The Role of Dr. Earl

At the end of 1939, Dr. McCutcheon retired from the post of medical superintendent, a post which he had held for nearly twenty years. The Board of Control paid tribute to him:

> *"His appointment as Medical Superintendent began a new era in the development of this Colony. During the period of his administration great progress has been made in this country in the institutional care and training of mentally defective persons, and Monyhull under Dr. McCutcheon's direction has played an important part in this movement. To his clear sighted, practical approach, and his ability and energy in solving administrative problems the Colony is greatly indebted."*

The Committee appointed Dr. C. J. C. Earl, F.R.C.P., D.P.M., as his replacement.

Dr. Earl has been deemed "one of the most brilliant and outstanding personalities in Mental Deficiency work" (Gunzburg 1959). He is credited with being able to make people "see the personality of the mental defective, which had disappeared behind a good deal of medical, biological and psychometric science"; to recognise the person behind the label. He viewed people with learning disabilities as having "the right to demand help, which could only be rendered by devoted personal assistance and not by providing larger and technically better equipped colonies." One colonist referred to him as "the greatest man I have ever known, he made a new man of me" (ibid.).

It was difficult at first for Dr. Earl to make many changes at Monyhull, due to the problems and shortages imposed by the war. Plans for development, particularly of the hostels, had to be put on hold. There were some staff changes. In 1942, Miss M. Parsons succeeded as matron. A psychologist was appointed as a part time teacher at the school and a psychiatric social worker was employed to visit the houses which the hostel women went to on daily licence. A weekly case conference between the medical and teaching staff was introduced. There were also changes in the organisation of the school, with the "lower grade" children being transferred to Marston Green or Coleshill Hall.

Dr. Earl's concerns lay with the problems of institutionalisation, and how they could be overcome to help people return to life in the community. He observed that "a well behaved lad, a good worker at an unskilled job, sent into society, may break down completely in a matter of days." He believed the problem to be one of change and its accompanying stress:

> *"Such institutionalised people live a completely routinised life and are content. Any alteration, even for the better, as for example an improvement in diet, may be resented. During the worst of the air raids period they protested if ordered from their job or, worse still, from their beds, to the safety of a refuge room. 'They ain't bombing us' was a frequent protest. These adults...showed no anxiety or fear of a danger which they could not comprehend. On the other hand, the wartime curtailment of the tobacco ration was violently resented"* (Earl 1956).

With an increasing number of patients going out to work in the wider community on licence, this was a difficult problem. Even with support and training, people who had adapted to private work in one area, would find it difficult to adapt to a different working environment:

> *"several young men, highly trained in housework, after succeeding brilliantly in private houses, broke down utterly in hotel work. Used to an individual employer, they could not adapt to orders from several members of staff, to say nothing of guests: "Too many bosses" as one lad succinctly expressed it, confuse them."*

Earl also recognised the effects that living in an institutional environment had upon communication and reasoning skills. People tended to adjust to a level "far below their potential". Much of his work was to concentrate upon the "educationally subnormal" child, "who was liable to become the certified adult defective unless helped in time" (Gunzburg 1959). He believed that:

> *"if these children could be diagnosed early and before they have broken down, and their education suitably graded, their logical capacity would rise with consequent benefit to their whole personality...Such a diagnosis would be a far more potent preventive of certifiable "mental deficiency" than any measure of compulsory or voluntary sterilisation"* (Earl 1956).

From 1940 to 1953, Dr. Earl worked to reorganise and improve one of the oldest custodial colonies in the country. Improvements were made in all aspects of people's lives. Patients' clothing was gradually "being modernised." Attempts were made to improve the food provided from the kitchens to the homes. Pocket money for those working inside the colony was introduced, "varying from 6d. to 3/- a week." All patients received a free issue of cigarettes and sweets. "Motor Coach" outings were arranged. Although these were small changes in themselves, they represented "a great advance" on the conditions that previously existed.

The custodial policies, inherent in the concept of a self sufficient colony, were gradually to change. They had facilitated life inside the colony, but not the training of people to live outside in the community. Earl developed the licencing system at Monyhull, so that people could go to work outside the colony rather than inside, wherever possible. By 1947, the Inspectors noted that 142 people were now on licence; "practically all of them are in some sort of situation or other and earning money." Positions ranged from domestic work in private houses, to industrial work in local firms. The wages that they received paid for their board and lodging, with the remainder as an allowance and savings. Of those on licence between 1945 and 1947, 24 male and 14 female patients were discharged from orders. Of those that were not on licence, "parole" was granted, which enabled them to leave the colony for half a day every week, "unless they are working outside the colony, in which case the conditions of parole apply throughout the week."

The 1946 NHS Act was to pass the control of the institution from the local council to the Minister of Health, and the mental deficiency colonies were to become hospitals. The change in status reflected the changes in policy. Dr. Earl accordingly turned Monyhull into "a leading progressive hospital, adjusted to a programme aimed at rehabilitation" (Gunzburg 1959).

Chapter 5

Monyhull Hospital

The National Health Service Act, 1946-8, reorganised and expanded the health and welfare services across the country. It aimed to distinguish between the "social welfare functions and the hospital functions of the old Public Assistance institutions, and to divide these functions between the new local authority welfare service and hospital service accordingly" (Jay Report 1979). All the old mental deficiency institutions were transferred to the NHS hospital authorities. Likewise, most community services for people with learning disabilities were to be provided by the local health authority, with the exception of day care facilities. The decision to place them within the health service was mainly because they were seen to be part of a wider mental health service. The government wanted to minimise the distinction between mental and physical health. It was recognised however, that there needed to be a complete review of mental health legislation, although this was not to occur for another eleven years.

Monyhull Colony therefore passed from Birmingham Corporation to the Ministry of Health, and together with Agatha Stacey Home at Rednal and the Midland Counties Institution at Knowle (Middlefield Hall), became a hospital group under the Birmingham Regional Hospital Board. Dr. Earl was appointed as the Chief Officer of the group.

The title of "hospital" replaced the outdated term "colony"; "patients" replaced "colonists". This symbolised the change in focus from purely custodial care towards training and rehabilitation for life in the wider community. Dr. Earl has been credited for his pioneering work in the field, but there was still a long road ahead. Although Monyhull had changed its administrative status, its patients were still living in an institution.

60031/82/9.

MINISTRY OF HEALTH,
32, Rutland Gate,
Knightsbridge,
London,
S.W.7.

2nd July, 1948.

Sir (Madam)

      I am directed by the Minister of Health to state that

he has directed that the   **Monyhull Colony** *AND ANCILLARY PREMISES AT:-*
THE LAURELS, 233, MONYHULL HALL RD, KING'S NORTON. BIRMINGHAM.
THE HAUNCH, HAUNCH LANE, BIRMINGHAM. 14.
shall be a mental deficiency institution for the purposes of the

Mental Deficiency Acts as amended by the National Health Service

Act, 1946.

I am, Sir (Madam)

    Your obedient Servant,

Frank Chant

The Superintendent,

Monyhull Colony   Mental Deficiency Institution.

(stamp: MONYHULL COLONY — 1 JUL 1948 — MEDICAL SUPERINTENDENT'S OFFICE)

(stamp: MONYHULL COLONY MED. SUPT. OFFICE — 3 JUL 1948)

Monyhull Colony certified as a mental deficiency institution under the NHS Act 1948.

A Training Environment

Very little had changed at Monyhull physically since the extension scheme was completed in 1925. The homes or villas, as they had been called in 1908, were now deemed old fashioned. Overcrowding was still a major problem, with 30% more patients than the standard accommodation provided. This prevented most attempts at modernisation. There was physically not enough room for all the patients and the facilities that they needed. New patients could only be admitted as a matter of urgency. Modernisation was desperately needed, as can be seen by the comments of the Board of Control Inspectors:

"It would seem that before 1939 decoration had been neglected and after that, little or nothing could be done... the furniture and general standard of comfort provided were obviously low...A consequence of this is that an impression of austerity and cheerlessness is given, and in order to overcome this a very large sum of money would be needed."

"The patients' living accommodation is dreary and lacks a homely atmosphere. Much of the furniture is obsolete and uncomfortable and the absence of curtains at most of the windows together with the bare wooden floors give the rooms a distinct barrack like look. There are practically no means of storing the men's clothes in a reasonable manner and the resulting effect of 'bundling' them at night is deplorable...one can find dormitories with beds arranged 'head to tail' or where there is no room between beds for a chair or a locker."

Quite apart from the fact that such a living environment was depressing, the authorities were also beginning to view it as an obstacle to rehabilitation. It was now recognised that "the hospital setting should be reorganised to become a preparatory stage before placement in normal conditions and to act as a transitional community where a planned programme is carried out for teaching 'living skills'" (Gunzburg 1970). An institutional environment only served to reinforce institutional attitudes and behaviour.

Renovation and modernisation began slowly in the 1950s, firstly under the guidance of Dr. Earl, and then by Dr. R. Stanley, the succeeding Medical Superintendent and Consultant Psychiatrist. Dr.

Nursing staff and the arrival of television.

Living room in one of the men's homes.

H. C. Gunzburg, Senior Clinical Psychologist was also to play a vital role.

Improvements were made slowly in the way of redecoration of the homes and the replacement of furniture, "especially the long institutional dining tables". There were new baths, wash basins and toilet facilities, "it was a far cry from the old cast iron cisterns and toilet pans" (Hill 1998). All the homes were provided with a wireless and then a television:

> *"TV made a big difference to the behaviour of patients. When they got bored or frustrated, they would abscond, and on being returned to the hospital, not being allowed to watch TV was a great deterrent. Mr Cowdrell supplied and fitted the TVs and maintained them when they got broken. In the early days there were no transistor radios, so one of the carpenter's jobs was making boxes to house the crystal sets, and it was a common sight to see patients sat up in bed with head phones on, listening to radio programmes" (ibid.).*

Living room in one of the women's homes.

Gas cookers were installed to replace the old coal ranges. A hairdressing salon was established, with the aim of providing additional training for the women. In 1958 a canteen was opened, "to be used as a club room for patients of both sexes", and therefore encouraging daily social contact between the two for the first time. Segregation was now being viewed as "quite artificial and undesirable because we all form part of a mixed society" (Stanley 1959), although it was some time before it was completely abolished.

The building of a new training workshop was also well underway. This latter development was the result of many years of work by Dr. Gunzburg. When Gunzburg was appointed Education and Training Officer in 1948, he recognised that the old workshops, relics of the 1914-1918 war, needed to be rebuilt as soon as conditions would allow. He began to reorganise the workshop activities, assisted by members of the nursing staff and students from the Department of Social Sciences at the University of Birmingham. The new Education and Training Department provided "vocational guidance, together with character and general educational training." Training was initially divided between a group of a dozen or more adolescent boys "in order to simplify their introduction to manual work from school life", and "a special low grade group". The Inspectors regarded the occupation and training of "low grade" patients to be "one of the most humanising functions that a colony can perform." Only male patients were involved however, due mainly to the lack of training facilities for the women.

The training programme focused on work of an industrial nature which was broken down into component parts. Each patient had an attainment chart on which his progress was marked weekly, by himself and by his instructor. This was to give purpose and continuity to the work, to encourage improvement and to give the patient "insight into his own capacities." The goal was "suitability for daily work" outside the hospital, initially on licence, but with a view to discharge.

The Board of Control applauded the initiative, reporting in 1956 that:

"Monyhull Hospital has over a period of years been creating and improving a system of organised occupation and training which has now become impressive. This is a collective effort on the part of doctors, psychologists, instructors and nurses. The figures are worth study. Of the 1,127 patients in residence 887 were occupied in some way and 176 were on licence. There are very few who are unoccupied for reasons other than age or physical disability. The figures for parole are exceptionally high. Occupation and training is not only extensive, but also...essentially practical in aim. For the higher grade patients this embraces training in industrial and other work within the hospital with a view to fitting such patients for and placing them in similar work outside. The same practical aim is shown in training low grade patients....As a result of our visit we were confirmed in our belief that this is one of the really important hospitals for mental deficiency in the country."

The new training workshops were opened by Sir Edward Thompson, Chairman of the Birmingham Regional Hospital Board, on 30 June 1959. The building had a capacity for 40 - 50 patients on two floors; the ground floor comprising the "low grade" workshop, shoe repairing and upholstering workshops; and the first floor, a tailoring workshop and a training unit for male adolescents. The aim of the workshops was outlined in the opening booklet:

Maintenance Workshops.

"These are activities which are related to the internal economy of the hospital. It is a valuable form of occupation and training, as it enables the longer stay patient to recognise his contribution to the community in which he is living. He is able to see the importance of his efforts in ensuring the well-being of his fellows. Even if his abilities are limited he still has something to offer to enrich the lives of his fellow colleagues and in so doing enrich his own. The tailoring workshop, the boot repairing workshop, the upholstering workshop and the dry cleaning plant are activities of this kind. The patients employed in these workshops are the low to medium grade, whose stay in hospital, for varying reasons, is likely to be lengthy."

Men at work in the new training workshops.

Workshops for Low Grade Patients.

"These activities are of the 'sheltered workshop' type. They are activities for the low grade - patients who by reason of their very limited abilities will never be able to be gainfully employed under the ordinary conditions existing in industry. They will always require the special conditions of a 'sheltered workshop', where speed of work, relationships with their instructors and with the persons working around them are specially designed to suit their needs. Each task has to be broken down to the simplest component so that they can confine their efforts to a single operation and not be confused by a multiplicity of manoeuvres. At the same time, this breakdown enables a small production line to be formed and underlines the importance of their efforts to each other. This interdependence can be appreciated by this grade of patient. Outwork from nearby factories plays a very important part in these sheltered workshops. It is a noticeable feature amongst the patients the interest they take in the use being made of the article which they are producing. The fact that it is an article used in the world at large is a spur to greater endeavour. Activities seen in this workshop include the making of paper bags, the making of industrial and domestic chamois leather mops, making of rugs, the

making of stools and children's chairs, and part of the processing of stool frames and coat hangers, which are sold to hospitals and various other authorities."

Unit for Male Adolescents.

"In this unit, known as the 'training school', an intensive rehabilitation and training programme is carried out, with the object of returning the young men to a full life outside the hospital in the shortest possible time. It is essential that his work habits and his ability to relate adequately to his employers and to his workmates should be satisfactory. The prime objective of this workshop is to emphasise these attitudes rather than to try and mirror the various operations which the young men may have to undertake when he returns to his place in industry. When the higher grade patient comes into hospital because of failure at work, often it has been found that it is not because he has been unable to acquire sufficient skills to carry out the type of work in which he was engaged, but resulted from bad work habits or an inability to get along with his foreman or workmates, due more to personality defects than simple lack of intelligence."

"To be able to enjoy a full life in the community other attributes are required as well as an ability to do a job of work. For this reason the unit utilises an extensive programme beyond the training in the workshop. Remedial education, (e.g. the 3 R's), training in social skills (e.g. learning how to use public services such as the Ministry of Labour, post offices, health services and national insurance), budgeting and thrift, personal hygiene, are all brought into the rehabilitation programme. Both individual and group psychotherapy is employed to improve the ability of these young men, so that they can get along better, not only with themselves but also the people they live with and meet at work and play."

"The patients in this workshop are medium to high grade. The atmosphere prevailing is as near as possible to what is found in industry, in tempo, discipline and the delegation to the patients of the responsibility for care of tools and machinery. Techniques in industry have been modified to enable them to carry out the more complicated tasks and at the same time profit from the experience of handling machinery in conjunction with their workmates. The jobs these patients are performing are in the main outwork from industry. They are of the heavier type and necessitate the use of machinery. That the jobs on which these patients are engaged is outwork from industry has a beneficial effect on their rehabilitation, because it emphasises in a concrete manner the target of rehabilitation, their return back to the community, and is yet another way of reducing their sense of separation from a world outside the hospital."

The training and active rehabilitation programmes carried out at Monyhull were seen to be enterprising and pioneering. This was a view shared not only by the Inspectors at the Board of Control in London, but also by health authorities across Britain and abroad.

The psychology department became the largest of its kind in mental deficiency hospitals around the country. In 1952, Dr. Gunzburg and Dr. Stanley amongst others, formed the Midland Mental Deficiency Society, later to become the British Society for the Study of Mental Subnormality. Its aim was to "provide an opportunity for the interchange of ideas on Mental Deficiency for all persons working and interested in this subject" (Annual Proceedings 1952-3). Membership was "open to all, whether they work in the hospital or in the community." Case conferences were held every week in collaboration with the local authority mental health department. Conferences were also held once a month to teach student nurses. The Journal of the Midland Mental Deficiency Society (becoming the British Journal of Mental Subnormality) was produced at Monyhull, with Dr. Gunzburg as editor until his retirement in 1979. It was to have a world wide circulation. Gunzburg's development of Progress Assessment Charts for use with people with learning disabilities, was also to gain worldwide acceptance.

Nursing Progress

The developments in training and rehabilitation meant that the role of the nurse was changing significantly. Previously, nurses had practised mainly a custodial approach, in keeping with the policies of the colony. Nurses would be "allocated a group of patients each day" and would accompany them to their place of work, either on the farm or gardens. Other patients were occupied in the homes, again supervised by a nurse (Kay 1976). A former member of staff recalled going to the homes to collect patients for work, where they (the patients) had to have "their fingernails and boots checked to see if they were clean." After work, staff would escort the patients back to their homes and "hand them over to the charge nurse." The patients were not allowed to walk around the grounds freely.

Women at work.

This role had been forced to some extent by a severe shortage of nursing staff, with only one or two members of staff caring for 50 - 60 patients. Nurses would work 54 hours a week on the day shift, and 60 at night. This was reduced to 44 hours in 1958.

Monyhull had been a recognised training school for nurses since 1927. In 1949, the training certificate for nurses changed to the Registered Nurse for the Mentally Subnormal (RNMS). Students worked and studied at Monyhull as well as Hollymoor and Highcroft hospitals as part of their training. They also gained experience in the occupational and training workshops. The nature of the training had changed to reflect the changes in attitude and policy towards people with learning disabilities. A varied syllabus was introduced with greater emphasis placed on social training and rehabilitation. Nursing assistants were also provided with a training scheme. In 1954, the Northern Ireland Hospital Authority contacted Monyhull with a view to training students for their first mental deficiency hospital, which was to open in three years time. 12 students from Northern Ireland

Nurse administering medicines.

Nativity play by children of St. Francis school.

were accepted for training as mental deficiency nurses. Nurses were also beginning to be actively recruited from the Commonwealth and other countries such as Mauritius, Malaysia and the Philippines, to cope with staff shortages.

Nurses then, began to take a more progressive role in the rehabilitation of patients who would finally be discharged to the community. They also cared for a large number of patients who, for reasons of physical or mental impairment, remained at the hospital. Many of these people had spent the greater part of their lives at Monyhull. It was now recognised that for long stay patients "simple storage or hotel keeping, however humane, can no longer be regarded as an adequate objective" (Stanley 1963). It was the duty of the nursing staff to help these people learn skills that would enable them to live as independently as possible within the hospital.

Holidays away from Monyhull were also introduced. The first of these were for the women who worked on daily licence, but they soon extended to the other patients. Patients would go for a week's holiday at Bognor, Rhyl or Colwyn Bay. It was the first holiday that most of them had ever had, and the first time that they had seen the sea:

"It was a major operation, with drugs, clothing, money etc, but nearly every week in the summer you would see a coach party go off, accompanied by staff" (Hill 1998).

The children were also taken on holidays to the seaside. Although the residential school at Monyhull had not passed to the NHS in 1946, being transferred to Birmingham City Education Department, the hospital continued to play a role in its management and provided many of its services until 1960. Among these was the provision of staff for the "treatment, supervision, control, feeding and clothing of the children." Nursing staff would care for the children outside of school hours, teach them basic 'home' skills such as sewing and darning, and take them on outings and holidays.

Nursing services were still strictly separated into male and female at this time, based on the policies of segregation. The Chief Male Nurse, Mr. Yardley, was in charge of the male staff and patients. Miss Parsons, the Matron was in charge of the female side. Working conditions were strict:

"Discipline was very stern; you only spoke when you were spoken to by a senior person. We were loathe to approach the ward office to ask a simple question. Looking at the case notes was out of the question, so we learnt about the patients the best way we could, usually by just asking them, or talking to older staff. Our work had to be completed before we went off duty and even though we may have finished at five, we would still be there at six if our work was not done. There was a strict order to ward routine. If you were given ten jobs to do, you had to complete them on double quick time. If, by some chance, you were to forget, for example, to put a certain label on a laundry bag, you were brought back from your room to do so; there was no argument."

"If you forgot your place for one moment in time and considered yourself an equal human being choosing to wish a senior person a 'Good Morning', you were suddenly reduced to worm size by the icy look you got. Sometimes we were close to tears by the attitude of our seniors, but there was always one of our fellow students who would mimic our seniors to a 'T' and have us in fits of laughter, relieving our frustration and tension and bringing humour to the patients' lives" (Anon. 1978).

After 18 years as matron and 40 years in the nursing service, Miss Parsons retired in 1959. She was awarded the M.B.E. for her dedication and services to nursing. Miss J. Moriarty was appointed as her successor. She was to be the last of the matrons, the post being replaced by the Head of Nursing Services in 1967. Miss Moriarty would also receive the M.B.E. upon her retirement in 1975.

"Like a Family"

Monyhull in the 1950s was very much regarded by staff as being "like a family." In fact, members of the same families would work together at Monyhull, and some were to meet their future husbands and wives there. For staff as well as patients, life was the hospital. Anyone coming to live and work at the hospital for the first time would have found themselves in a self contained community.

"The hospital was approached from Monyhull Road, through two big metal gates which were propped open, and a side gate for pedestrians. A stone built lodge was just

The main entrance at Monyhull.

inside the gates which housed a switchboard, manned 24 hours a day. There was also a lodgekeeper who dealt with the time cards as all ancillary staff had to clock in and out. He also acted as a receptionist for anyone calling at the hospital. The deputy hospital engineer lived in the staff house just inside the grounds; Mr Yates who was on call 24 hours a day. In front of the staff house was a weigh bridge and most of the lorries delivering to the hospital had to be weighed in and out. To the right of the main entrance lay the reception home, used for patients who were being admitted for the first time. This building was later converted to living accommodation, housing doctors and nursing staff...The children's side housed the hospital administrator, who kept a sturdy eye on the running of the hospital" (Hill 1998).

Many members of staff lived at Monyhull. Some, including the Chief Nurse and Matron, leased one of the hospital properties. Others lived in the nurses' homes, which were strictly segregated and regulated:

"Nurses had to be in by 11 p.m. and were allowed one late pass per week until midnight; then you had to sign a passbook to prove you were back in the nurses home.

Matron's party.

Cinema at the assembly hall.

And if, by some misfortune, you were late, you had to report to Matron's office the following morning for a brisk telling off." (Anon.).

Although the staff lived and worked in what would today be regarded as strict conditions, Monyhull was seen to be their home. They lived there, worked there and socialised there. The assembly hall was "one of the main stays of hospital life" for both staff and residents:

"There is an excellent stage in the hall and outside artists, concert parties and choirs have given first-class entertainment to the patients here. In addition to this, many fine shows have been given by the staff and higher grade patients, particularly the annual pantomime which was produced by an assistant matron, Miss Poole and later by Miss Hankin. A brass band was also formed amongst the male nursing staff, and here again a few of the male patients were trained to play various instruments and qualified for membership in the band. Besides concert work, this band provided music on the recreation field on sports days, and early on Christmas morning, as the 'waits', the band made a complete tour of the colony, playing carols and hymn tunes outside the various homes. Cinema shows are also held in the assembly hall as well as mixed dances and

Sports Day 1956.

parties. *During the Christmas season, this hall is tastefully decorated and becomes the centre for all main parties given to the adults and children in turn, also the annual staff social evening given by the Hospital Staff Social Club is held in this hall" (Rogers 1972).*

"Every year a staff dinner was held in the assembly hall, waited on by the kitchen staff, who had theirs the next day. Staff were allowed to go home early to change, for it was a best bib and tucker do. Each head of department gave a speech on what had been done in the previous year and what was hoped for in the future, very enlightening as to future plans. A free and easy concert was held afterwards, and was one of the main functions of the year, enjoyed by all. Norman Evans, a famous comedian, brought his stage show to the hospital, and was broadcast from the stage of the assembly hall to a lunch time audience on the radio. Staff and patients made up the audience in the assembly hall" (Hill 1998).

There were also outside facilities for recreation, including a large boating lake, tennis courts, football and cricket pitches. Regular sports matches against other hospitals and the annual sports day, were a highlight for staff and residents:

Harry Smith, Head Cowman with "Billy" the Kingswood Bull 1953.

Monyhull staff and horse before motor transport.

"One big day in the year for us was our sports day. This was the day when all the boys and girls and men and women could get together for an enjoyable afternoon for sports. The Lord Mayor and Lady Mayoress always attended to present prizes to the winners and at the end of the afternoon would give a trophy to each winning home. The events would end with a fancy dress parade and the costumes were always very good. After a high tea in the home we would come back on the field and wander round the sideshows or listen or dance to Monyhull's own brass band which used to play for many years. A good time was had by all" (Jordan 1976).

Monyhull was a community in itself. It still produced most of its own food with the help of the two farms and the bakehouse. It had its own carpenters, upholsterers, shoemakers, sewing room, laundry, engineers and transport. Staff and patients worked together to keep the hospital running. The two churches provided services for those of both Roman Catholic and Protestant faiths. Entertainment and recreation were provided. However, Monyhull was no longer a closed community. The gates were opening up to the world outside.

Working Together

A staff committee was formed to consider and make recommendations about working conditions, the welfare of patients and staff, and to promote efficiency and good working relations. One of the initiatives was to hold a 'Publicity Week', where the public and press would be invited to visit the hospital and see what was being achieved. It was an enormous step towards opening up relations between the hospital and the wider community. Invitations were sent to parents and relatives, local organisations, employers of patients on daily licence and pupils from local schools. From 24 - 30 May 1954, visitors were able to go on conducted tours of the hospital, see exhibitions of work, and attend a concert put on by the patients. The week was a huge success and resulted in several offers of direct help. Among these was the idea of a 'Friends of Monyhull' group, started by Mr Reynolds, a charge nurse, who wanted "to buy extras for the lads on his ward, which housed a number of patients with a poor quality of life" (Hill 1998).

The League of Friends held its inaugural meeting two months later. It was established to support and befriend those patients who were without relatives or friends outside of the hospital, and to develop an important contact with the community. Over the years it was to play a vital role in the lives of many people at Monyhull, organising fund raising events, dances and outings, providing friendship and support.

Parents and relatives were also being encouraged to become more involved in the care of patients. In 1957, the following procedures were outlined:

"As soon as a patient is admitted it is explained to him and his parents that the purpose of his stay in hospital is to equip him, by training, to live an independent life in the community as soon as he is ready for it. Parole is freely used; in fact the attitude of the staff is that it is an ordinary right which is 'restored' to the patient soon after admission, and not 'given' like something new. From the start, very careful steps are taken to keep parents informed; the hospital social worker calls on them within a few days after the patients admission, to answer questions and explain the position generally; and the parents are also seen by the medical superintendent within a few weeks and are

reassured that licence or discharge will be spontaneously granted as soon as it is due, without the need for pressure from them. In those cases in which admission has been the result of a representation that the patient is in need of care and training which cannot be provided in his home, it is customary to assure the parents that discharge will be granted at any time if they request it."

Parents were encouraged to visit and to take patients home at the weekend, as often as possible. They were advised well in advance of any changes in arrangements concerning their relative. A Parents' Group was formed in 1959 to help improve co-operation and communication between the hospital and relatives. By 1961 it had more than a hundred members, providing help with activities within the hospital, and also acting as a support group for the relatives themselves. Although separate from the League of Friends, the two groups worked closely together, forming the Earl Foundation in 1964. This was a registered charity, established to provide holidays for children and adults with learning disabilities, their friends and their families. Mr. Roy Hull, Chairman of the Earl Foundation and Treasurer of the League of Friends, was among those who dedicated themselves, not only to the people living at Monyhull, but to people with learning disabilities everywhere.

The opening up of Monyhull and its links with the local community were further enhanced by the activities of the church. The church, dedicated to St. Francis in November 1948 by the Bishop of Birmingham, was always well attended, both by patients and visitors. People were "impressed by the excellent and hearty singing which is rarely heard in our churches today" (Rogers 1972). Under the guidance of the Chaplain, Canon Dunn and then the Revd. Skinner, a choir of women patients and boys from the residential school was formed. In 1950, the community hymn singing by the patients, staff, and the choirs of Kings Norton and West Heath, was broadcast live by the BBC. A few years later, another service was broadcast for Mental Health Week with a sermon by the Dean of Westminster.

April 1958 saw the 50th anniversary of the opening of Monyhull, which was commemorated with a special church service, open day and exhibition for the public, and a fete day for the patients and staff.

The commemoration brochure reviewed the last 50 years and concluded:

"The history of changing activities and practice in the care and treatment of mentally defective patients over the last fifty years has been mirrored in the work of Monyhull. The hospital takes justifiable pride in knowing that not only has it always been numbered among the progressive Mental Deficiency Institutions in England but also because from its beginning to the present date it has often led the way in fresh advances. The report of the Royal Commission on the Law relating to mental illness and mental deficiency indicates that the future holds possibilities of great changes. The public consciousness has become alive to the needs of people mentally less well endowed; a willingness to show understanding and tolerance of their shortcomings is rapidly spreading and specialists from many different fields are now developing new methods of treatment and training."

The recommendations of the Royal Commission were indeed far reaching and were to significantly change the role of Monyhull and mental deficiency hospitals around the country.

Chapter 6

The Mental Health Act 1959

The report of the Royal Commission on the law relating to mental illness and mental deficiency was published in 1957. It made extensive recommendations as to the certification, detention, care, absence on trial or licence, discharge and supervision of people with a mental illness or learning disability, which were to significantly change the face of future services. The existing Lunacy, Mental Treatment and Mental Deficiency Acts were deemed to be old fashioned and no longer appropriate. In particular, it was no longer believed that 'persons of unsound mind' and 'defectives' must be certified and detained in special institutions in order to receive treatment. The report recommended that people should be treated as voluntary patients without certification and detention, unless "it was in their own interests or those of other people or society in general that they should be removed for treatment even against their will" (Watkin 1975). Furthermore, the report stated that it was:

"not now generally considered in the best interests of patients who are fit to live in the general community that they should be in large or remote institutions such as the present mental and mental deficiency hospitals. Nor is it a proper function of the hospital authorities to provide residential accommodation for patients who do not require hospital or specialist services."

The role of the mental deficiency hospital was therefore to provide in-patient and out-patient services only for those who needed specialist medical treatment or continual nursing care. The aim of treatment was to enable the patient to live in the wider community and no patient was to remain in hospital once he had reached that stage and had a "reasonably good home to go to." The local authorities were to take responsibility for the provision of services and care in the community.

Mr Yardley, Chief Male Nurse saying goodbye to a patient 1959.

The report also recommended another change in the classification of patients. The term 'mentally ill patients' was to replace 'persons of unsound mind'; the term 'psychopathic patients' was to include any type of aggressive or inadequate personality including feebleminded or moral defectives; the term 'severely subnormal patients' was to replace the terms 'idiot' and 'imbecile'. In addition, the term 'mental defective' was no longer to be used.

The recommendations of the Royal Commission led to the passing of the Mental Health Act 1959, with only a few alterations including the introduction of the term 'subnormal patient' to replace that of 'feebleminded.' It was now the duty of the authorities to implement the changes incurred.

In general, Monyhull welcomed the changes brought about by the Mental Health Act. They were seen in many ways only to "give expression to opinions voiced as long ago as 1934 by Dr. Earl" and "set the seal of official approval on the idea that the hospitals should be places where patients are treated and not stored" (Stanley 1959).

Nevertheless, there were some concerns. It was now the responsibility of the local authorities to provide the necessary help, support and supervision once active nursing care or treatment was no longer required. However, it would be many years before comprehensive services could be established. It was feared that patients would be discharged into the community where the support they needed would not be provided. In the past, this had been achieved by the use of licence, often for lengthy periods, until the patient was deemed capable of living in the community unaided or with help from family and friends.

Following the Act, all patients detained under order had to be reclassified. Monyhull had in fact reviewed its patients in 1958 on the recommendations of the Royal Commission. Sixty per cent of the people at Monyhull were 'decertified', but were to remain in hospital as informal patients. Very few discharged themselves or were removed by relatives against advice. The hospital regarded the change to informal status as being: *"of overwhelming benefit in enabling doctors to establish a proper professional relationship with patients. The changes have inevitably increased the patient's dignity as a human individual. Not only is this right ethically, but it helps to create the correct setting for treatment" (ibid.).*

The Act meant that in time Monyhull would develop a new role. Training and occupation centres would eventually be provided by the local authorities in the community. Once these were established, it was thought that the majority of patients admitted to Monyhull would be "those unsuitable for such an occupational centre due to mental instability or antisocial conduct" (Stanley 1959). New admissions would also include those detained by order through the courts. This raised certain problems, as Monyhull had previously been run on an open ward policy, with no facilities for detention as such. It was not a 'secure hospital' but would have to provide a degree of security for those patients that required it.

In reality, changes in service provision were slow to come about: *"The Act is still many years ahead of public opinion. The major switch to community care made possible in the Act appears to be a thing which will only take place very slowly" (Stanley 1961).*

In the meantime, Monyhull continued to provide training and

rehabilitation for those who needed it, whether they were in-patients, out-patients or day patients. It also provided continual nursing care for long stay, "chronically ill", and increasingly elderly patients. In 1963, it was estimated that up to three quarters of the population at Monyhull were "certainly here for life."

Design for Life

For the 'severely subnormal' patients, the elderly and 'severely handicapped', Monyhull was considered to be a permanent home. At the time, it was not deemed possible for these people to be rehabilitated into the community. Instead, greater efforts were put into making life in the hospital as comfortable and as homely as possible. It was recognised that the traditional 'ward', with rows of beds on either side (and sometimes down the middle) was not an acceptable or appropriate living environment. Institutional settings and practices needed to be replaced. Dr. Stanley, Dr. Gunzburg and

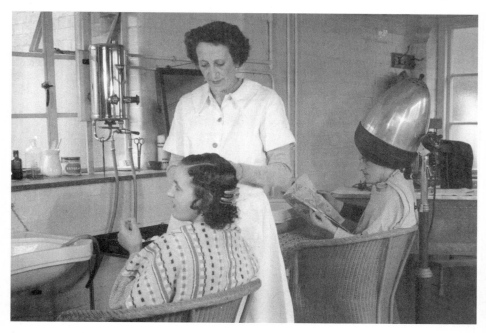

Visiting the hairdressing salon.

Residents enjoying a game of snooker.

Mr. Twist, the engineer, worked together to try and make this a reality. This was no easy task in an overcrowded hospital and with no extra money to provide additional accommodation.

Improvements had begun in the 1950s, with the redecoration programmes, the removal of the long communal dining tables, and the upgrading of facilities. The idea was to gradually replace the ward with "small living units with a few beds, with opportunities for putting personal possessions away, with tables and comfortable chairs, with the small domestic touches, flower vases, pictures and wireless to create a 'home atmosphere' for those destined to spend their lives there" (Hospital Management Committee 1960). A trial of the 'living units' idea was first carried out at Middlefield Hospital, one of the institutions in the Monyhull group:

"By a careful arrangement of specially designed lockers, for hanging and storing patients' belongings, the former large wards have been broken up into small living and

resting spaces comprising four to six beds. The locker arrangements are flexible and adjustable and permit easy communication between the various units. There is space for vases of flowers, pictures and personal treasures and this, together with the decorations, helps considerably in producing a more normal home atmosphere than commonly found in institutions for the severely handicapped"(ibid.).

Each home was to have "carpets on the floor, wallpaper in all rooms, a far cry from the austerity of the 50s. No more green and brown paint, pastel colours were the order of the day. Most homes installed tropical fish aquariums to give a peaceful atmosphere" (Hill 1998). However, a more normal home atmosphere did not just consist of a better physical environment. Over the years, institutional practices had suppressed expressions of individuality and the exercise of personal choice. Simple improvements could be made, for example, with the introduction of menus, so that people could choose what they wanted to eat rather than simply accepting what they were given. Clothing and footwear could be personalised. The Committee encouraged the acquisition of personal clothing but conceded that "since the homes were built some 50 years ago and overcrowding constitutes a major problem, there is little or no space for adequate storage, which would give all patients an opportunity for exercising immediate control over all their belongings." Similarly, the costs of radically changing the traditional institutional buildings, furniture, clothing etc., were 'prohibitive' and it was recognised that changes would have to come about in small steps.

The 'upgrading' of the homes was to take over twenty years to complete. By 1970 however, all of the patients had their own personal clothes and footwear, although they were still ordered and issued by the hospital stores. It was recognised that: *"the one great thing that was missing in our patients' clothing set-up was the lack of facilities to give our patients the personal service...it was so impersonal the way we had to issue the clothing. What we were looking for was a shop where the patients could visit and select their clothing and be fitted up" (Snape 1975).*

The clothing shop did not become a reality until 1975, but represented a great advance for mental deficiency hospitals:

"To be able to say to a male patient, 'You can choose your own shirt, tie, pullover, trousers, jackets, pyjamas, footwear,' or to the female patient, 'your dress, coat etc.' is as

great for the shop staff as it is for the patient. At long last we are able to treat our patients as individual human beings, and not just as faceless patients that have to put up with the first thing that comes to hand and trusting to luck whether it is the right size garment" (*ibid*).

Social Education

During the 1960s, there was a move towards social and educational programmes to enable patients to experience, understand and act upon the world around them. The aim was to develop the skills and potential of all the people living at Monyhull. This included preparing to live and work in the wider community where possible, and promoting individual capabilities and independence for those who would remain within the hospital.

The Education department was formed in 1960 after the residential school became completely separate from the hospital. Dr Gunzburg, Director of Psychology, took responsibility for the department until a full time Education Officer was appointed. Four part time teachers

Boys learning 'feeding' skills.

Children learning to cross the road.

were also later employed by Kings Heath Adult Education Institute. The department offered widespread tuition at a time when access to further education in the community was severely limited.

Much of the traditional '3 R' work of reading, writing and mathematical skills was initially: *"reduced to bare essentials, partly on account of time, and also because feelings of success can be better achieved by striving for more easily obtainable goals. For example, the teaching of reading to non-readers is limited to the acquirement of Social Sight Vocabulary which includes 200 words of social importance eg. Danger, Exit, Wet Paint, No Smoking" (Hospital Management Committee 1960).* For many patients, being able to sign their name or recognise coins was a great achievement.

The education and psychology departments worked together with nursing staff to develop suitable individual programmes. Although the establishment of more homely settings in itself did not transform institutional life, the conversion of wards to 'living units' was seen to offer "natural learning opportunities" for patients, with the nurse as a "social educator" (Gunzburg 1970). Much of this work was devoted to teaching daily living skills such as personal hygiene, cooking, going shopping, using the telephone, visiting the post office etc. A series of books called 'Life in the Community' were specially written to help people with such subjects as 'Landladies', 'First Day at Work' and 'Post Office Savings'.

Practical experience was most important:

> *"First in small groups, then individually the patients are made familiar with the everyday tasks of using public transport, visiting the post office for different types of transactions, going shopping, telephoning etc. More interviews with employers and foremen have been tape recorded and visual aids are of particular importance in this work. Cooking and housework classes are shared by both sexes and personal hygiene has been introduced for girls"* (Hospital Management Committee 1960).

Outside of work and training, patients were encouraged to choose for themselves how to spend their time. The extensive use of 'parole' enabled many to leave the hospital grounds and "mix freely with the outside world" without the restrictions or supervision imposed in the

Women residents going to work.

past. Social skills training therefore included learning to live in a mixed society and the segregation of patients in the hospital was consequently reviewed. Previously, male and female patients had only been able to mix at certain social functions, such as dances, or sports and fete days. The opening of the canteen for both patients and staff had begun a relaxation of traditional policy. For the first time, natural social relationships between patients and staff, men and women were actively encouraged:

"Various attempts to encourage more natural social relationships between the sexes have been taken by the hospital. A canteen in the hospital grounds with a number of tables and chairs is open throughout the day to staff and patients of both sexes who meet there quite naturally. No restrictions are imposed on their mixing, and to see girls and boys sharing a table is quite a normal feature. Men and women meet frequently and informally on the way to and from work, in the hospital and at various social occasions like pictures and dances. In the evenings some female homes have whist drives and other games to which they invite male patients. There is a mixed club for patients working outside the hospital and visits to theatres and other clubs in the area take place regularly. In the educational classes men and women attend at the same time and no difficulties have arisen over this arrangement"

Male residents outside Home 3.

"Normal living takes place in a mixed community. Men and women are generally happier and better where it is possible for them to share their life and activities with each other" (Hospital Management Committee 1960).

Scaling Down

Changing attitudes and policies were sweeping across the whole of hospital life. There was increasing emphasis on patient rights. The National Association for Mental Health reported on the dangers of exploiting patients as cheap labour, and stated that all therapeutic work programmes should be tailored to individual needs. It was therefore no longer thought appropriate that patients be employed in general domestic work in the hospital. Domestic staff began to be recruited, relieving patients and the nursing staff of certain duties. Female domestic staff were introduced to the male homes, which represented a considerable change in attitude, and was regarded by the Committee as "a most successful innovation." It was also suggested that female nursing staff be employed in male homes. This was in part due to a lack of qualified male staff, but also reflected the change in attitude towards segregation of the sexes. The two nursing services eventually combined to form one. Mr Yardley, the Chief Male Nurse, retired in 1967 and was not replaced. Miss Moriarty, the former Matron became the single Head of Nursing Services.

The change in approach to work and training could also be seen in the development of the workshops. There was a move towards more 'industrial' type work and unskilled labour "to prepare for work generally rather than for any one job in particular" (Hospital Management Committee 1960). Although this had initially been introduced on a limited basis, it was gradually extended to include most of the patients in the hospital. Work was brought in from local firms:

"There was a lot of outwork done for a firm called Metal Smallwares, saucepan knobs for the lids, that sort of stuff. And there was a contract to make women's hair curlers, hair grips and so on. The patients would sit there in the day putting the foam on plastic frames or putting the little plastic pins that went through a curler. There were literally

thousands and thousands of them" (Anon.).

This type of work was slowly to replace the traditional trades of shoe repairing, upholstering, rug and basket making etc. which were now deemed old fashioned. As a consequence, many of the traditional industries at Monyhull began to close down. The bakehouse was amongst the first to go in 1961. Without the help of the patients, it simply became too expensive for the hospital to produce its own bread.

The gardens were to suffer too. As the number of people employed as gardeners dropped, it was impossible to maintain the grounds as before: *"Most of the trees were removed from around the hospital, flower beds were grassed over for easing mowing, and the flower garden was filled over. There were no longer any cut flowers for the homes and the last of the greenhouses was demolished" (Hill 1998).*

The farms were to face a similar fate. Since the opening of Monyhull, they had provided work for many of the men and women who lived there, and supplied much of the food:

"There was Bells farm which is still there now, which was the pig farm for bacon and pork. Kingswood farm was situated at the Maypole, that was the main farm, with the dairy supplying all the milk, and the fowls for the eggs. It also supplied probably a hundred per cent of the potatoes which were used. Quite a few of the patients worked up there...they would rather be at the farm than back at the ward" (Anon.).

However, by 1962 the farms were no longer deemed suitable for occupation and training purposes. The Management Committee felt unable to justify farming by the hospital:

"It could not be said that farming was essential to provide occupation for a substantial number of patients which could not be found in some other form within the hospital. Present day thought did not consider that psychiatric hospitals should be completely isolated from the community and it was not now felt that a large area of land should be retained in order to provide seclusion for the hospital."

The farms were to close. All the land south of the brook, between the eastern edge of the estate and the old lake, and west of the lake to St.

Upon instructions from Monyhull Hospital Management Committee.

Bells & Kingswood Farms,

Kings Heath, Birmingham 14

DISPERSAL SALE BY PUBLIC AUCTION OF THE

ENTIRE

LIVE AND DEAD FARMING STOCK

comprising:

76 DAIRY & STORE CATTLE

TWO PEDIGREE BULLS

FRIESIAN BULL
"JAMES FARM ROSQUAL"

HEREFORD BULL
"SKILTS TURPIN"

232 Breeding & Fattening PIGS

PEDIGREE L.W. BOAR

Farm Implements and Effects

Dairy Equipment   120 Tons of Hay (in Lots)

TO BE SOLD BY AUCTION

on

SATURDAY, 28th AUGUST, 1965

at 11.0 a.m. promptly BY

LUCE & SILVERS

TUDOR HOUSE, BROMSGROVE

Tel.: 5234 (3 lines)

Sale of Bells and Kingswood Farms 1965.

Aerial view of the Monyhull estate.

Francis school, (excluding the farm buildings at Kingswood and Bells Farm), was declared redundant. It was sold to the Birmingham City Corporation for housing development. The farms were gradually run down and ceased activity in 1965. The animal stock, farming implements and equipment were sold by public auction. The Farm Bailiff and some of the farm workers were redeployed as gardeners for the hospital group, and continued to grow some of the vegetables. Kingswood farm buildings, which had been initially excluded from sale, were deemed unsuitable for conversion into accommodation for patients. In 1968 they were declared derelict and were demolished. Bells farmhouse remains standing, and was restored to its former glory in 1989.

The land between St. Francis school and the Cottage was also declared surplus to hospital requirements and sold. In 1969, the Cottage which was previously the home of the medical superintendent, became a hostel for both male and female patients. It replaced The Laurels, which was closed down. The Monyhull estate was gradually diminishing.

Changing Policies

The 1960s had seen a number of attempts to improve the lives of people with learning disabilities, both in the hospitals and in the community. Considerable changes had been brought about by the Mental Health Act, with the shift towards voluntary, short term and out-patient treatment and rehabilitation, and advances in the use of antipsychotic and anticonvulsant medication. The emphasis was now on community care, with training centres, sheltered workshops and residential services to be provided by the local authorities. The hospital was to provide specialist medical and nursing care only. In practice, these developments were slow to materialise. There was simply not enough money to establish the services needed to provide comprehensive support in the community, so the hospital continued to play the leading role.

At Monyhull, progress was being made within the hospital, with gradual changes in attitudes and policy. From 1958, there had been a drive towards making life in the hospital as similar as possible to life outside the hospital. This extended to both living and working conditions and practices. It reflected to some extent the 'normalisation principle', which gained worldwide recognition in 1969. The 'normalisation principle' was developed to "make available to the mentally subnormal the patterns and conditions of everyday life which are as close as possible to the norms and patterns of mainstream society" (Nirje 1970). They were further developed by Gunzburg in the 1970s, who introduced the additional processes of 'personalisation' and 'socialisation'. In the US, Wolfensberger began to use them as a yardstick against which services could be planned and evaluated. For the first time, people were asking "How would an ordinary member of the community view what was going on here?" and comparing the lives of people with learning disabilities to their own (O'Brien and Tyne 1981).

In 1967, The News of the World published allegations of cruelty and malpractice at Ely Hospital, a psychiatric hospital for people with learning disabilities and the mentally ill in Cardiff. The inquiry that followed drew public attention to the reality facing many such hospitals, including severe shortages of qualified staff and a grave lack of financial resources. Money had to be made available if improvements and developments were to be implemented.

As a result of the Ely Report, resources began to be reallocated to the hospitals, and the Hospital Advisory Service was established to provide independent inspections. Minimum standards were drawn up and issued to the Hospital Boards. These included improvements to staff:patient ratios, reduction of overcrowded wards, the introduction of interdisciplinary meetings and staff training schemes, and an increase in the numbers of domestic staff (Jay 1979).

Monyhull was no exception and was to make the necessary changes in order to meet the new regulations. This was now the task of the newly formed South Birmingham Hospital Management Committee. Due to a regrouping of hospitals, on 31st March 1969 the administration of the Monyhull Group and Selly Oak Hospital was combined.

The last Monyhull Hospital Management Committee (HMC) 1969.

Chapter 7

Better Services

In 1971, the newly elected Conservative government produced the White Paper "Better Services for the Mentally Handicapped". The paper built on the reforms introduced by the Mental Health Act in 1959, which over ten years later, had been slow to materialise. Local authorities with limited resources had had to start from scratch to provide community residential and day services for people with learning disabilities. By 1969, there was still a huge shortfall in community provision and an estimated 60 000 still lived in long stay hospitals. The paper acknowledged that:

"the main effect of the shortage of residential places combined with a shortage in many areas of training centres and of social workers, is that some families with mentally handicapped members living at home have to continue under almost unbearable stress and many hospitals are under unrelenting pressure to admit more patients to already overcrowded wards."

Almost all of the existing hospitals suffered from overcrowding. Facilities were outdated and inadequate for the needs of an increasingly elderly and more severely handicapped population. Already understaffed, nurses were faced with greater demands than ever before.

The White Paper re-emphasised that mentally handicapped people should not be unnecessarily segregated from the wider community, and should have access to the same services as the general population, with additional specialist help as required. Existing mental handicap hospitals were to provide in-patient services for those who were unable to remain in the family or residential home and who required specialist treatment, training and care. It was envisaged that these services would be for those with additional physical or mental impairments. Hospitals would also provide day services for those who needed specialist services but were still able to live at home. This would help to reduce the number of in-patient admissions and provide continuity of care following discharge.

Services were to be provided by a range of professionals working closely together to meet individual patient's needs. This included not only clinical services but education, industrial and occupational therapy, and leisure activities. Specialist staff would include doctors, nurses, psychologists, physiotherapists, occupational therapists, speech and language therapists and education officers. It was recommended that social workers be used to ensure close collaboration between hospital and social services. More use was also to be made of voluntary services to maintain the links between the hospital and the local community. Volunteers were seen to play an essential role in the lives of patients, especially those who were without friends or relatives. It had been estimated that a third of patients in long stay hospitals never received visitors (Watkin 1975).

£40 million was allocated to services for the mentally handicapped. This was to be spent on reorganising services, and reducing the number of people living in hospitals by up to fifty per cent. No new large hospitals for the mentally handicapped were to be built, and existing hospitals were to improve substandard conditions.

Living in Hospital

Monyhull therefore faced the task of improving conditions and services within the hospital and reducing the number of in-patient beds. Overcrowding had been a major problem at Monyhull since the first world war. Over sixty years later, the hospital was still battling to reduce the number of beds in each of the homes, in the face of increasing pressure to admit more patients. The reorganisation of the NHS in 1974, had only added to the problem. Five new Health Districts (North, South, East, West and Central) had been established, each based on a District General Hospital, to form Birmingham Area Health Authority. Monyhull was part of the newly formed South Birmingham Health District based on Selly Oak Hospital. However, being the only mental handicap hospital in the area, it now had to

Monyhull hostels.

provide services for the whole of the new Birmingham District. The pressure on beds and services was enormous.

There had been a continuous programme to reduce overcrowding. The number of people being discharged was by now far greater than the number of people being admitted. This had previously been aided by the use of the outlying hostels, which helped patients to develop the skills necessary for them to leave the hospital and return to the community. In 1974, a pre-discharge unit at the Haunch was also established, providing an extra 20 beds. On the other hand, new admissions tended to be more highly dependent, with a greater degree of mental and physical impairment than in previous years. An

The day hospital.

A shared day room

increased proportion had additional behavioural problems. It was agreed that further admissions could not be catered for without a significant increase in nursing staff and accommodation. This was not forthcoming. To cope with the mounting pressure from the community, a Crisis Intervention Team was formed, comprising a doctor, nurse and social worker. The team would see referrals from GPs and social services, and visit people in the community when a crisis arose, helping to reduce unnecessary hospital admissions. A day hospital was also opened for people living in the community who needed the support services provided within the hospital, but who did not need to be admitted. To help ease the accommodation difficulties, a general medical ward was established on the hospital site, providing another 56 beds for the care of the sick elderly and physically handicapped.

By 1976, and for the practically the first time since Monyhull had opened, the number of beds on each home had been reduced to an average of 35. However, although this was undoubtedly an improvement on previous conditions, residents still had to sleep in 'wards' rather than in smaller and more homely living units. The programme to upgrade the homes was continuing but had been slowed by economic constraints and it would be many years before it was finally completed. A report produced by the Joint Liaison Group at Monyhull in 1978, noted that the hospital still had "inadequate beds and facilities for the functions it performs" and it was suggested that:

> *"although many of the restrictions imposed on living units by certain administrative regulations do much to hinder the 'homeliness' of the wards…personnel could go a long way to improving this factor if they introduced more personal items into the environment in the form of pictures, ornaments etc. and also the facilities needed for patients to keep personal items." (Lawson 1978).*

Despite the emergence and worldwide acceptance of the principles of normalisation, institutional conditions and practices lingered on in the long stay hospitals. Resources were stretched to the limit and attitudes were notoriously slow to change.

Meeting Patients Needs

The recommendations of the White Paper and the changes in the patient population at Monyhull also led to concern that the training, occupation and recreation facilities provided were no longer meeting patients' needs. The Joint Liaison Group found that:

> *"The fact that the training department only offers six different activities, three of which require enlargements, suggests that insufficient planning has been carried out into what facilities patients should be given, rather than what facilities staff are willing to give. No one has questioned the usefulness or practicality of the types of training mentioned, nor indeed what is involved in some of them. The hospital needs to discuss its feelings regarding different forms of training and therapy and to adopt a commonly accepted policy and strategy to patient care within Monyhull." (Lawson 1978).*

A working party was therefore convened, consisting of Dr Bainton, Consultant Psychiatrist, Mr. Dewhurst, Senior Nursing Officer, and Mr. Jones-Owen, Senior Clinical Psychologist. They provided the first systematic review of training and recreational needs and provision at Monyhull.

By 1979, there was a total of 552 residents at Monyhull, of whom 107 lived in the outlying hostels. For many of those who lived at the hospital, daytime occupation was still focused on the type of industrial work that had been introduced in the 1950s and 60s, "when the type of patient we were caring for then, plus the favourable economic and social climate in the country enabled us to discharge many patients into local industry and residential accommodation". However, needs and conditions had changed and industrial work was now deemed to be unsuitable for the majority of residents.

By the end of the 70s, training and recreation were provided in a number of different ways, in a number of different settings and with a number of different professionals involved. There were now three workshops on the hospital site, catering for over 150 people. Two of the workshops had been purpose built in 1959 for industrial therapy and light assembly work, and were still being used as such. The more recently built third workshop had been purpose built for occupational therapy and was mainly given over to women's handicrafts. There were however, no qualified occupational therapists working at Monyhull. In general, training and recreation programmes were carried out by nursing staff. A small number of residents worked alongside the ancillary staff, as carpenters, painters, gardeners, and porters.

Education continued to be provided by the Education Officer, with classes in literacy, numeracy, oral communication, and social sight vocabulary. A library for the residents had also been introduced. The Kings Heath Institute of Further Education provided classes in swimming, PE, metalwork, art and crafts. Some residents attended a social rehabilitation course at Bournville College.

Off site, the hostels continued to provide social education and training, leading up to discharge where possible. Residents of Agatha Stacey were involved in a personal development course, with the help of a group of young people from a local comprehensive school. Regular contact with the school was seen to be of benefit not only to the residents, but also for the pupils, who gained a valuable learning experience. The Cottage provided social skills training to prepare for transfer to the pre-discharge unit at the Haunch. The pre-discharge unit helped residents to develop a range of skills, including budgeting, shopping, cooking and general household management. Residents in the hostels also had greater access to a wide range of recreational and educational facilities.

For those living within the hospital, recreation was provided both on and off site. Annual holidays were now taken by over half of the residents, and most were able to enjoy day trips. Evenings out to restaurants, the cinema, the theatre, and the pub were also introduced, although staffing levels dictated how often these could be enjoyed. This also meant that residents would sometimes only be able to go out in large groups. Onsite, recreation tended to be centred on the activities of the patients' club and canteen, the church or the individual homes.

However, in 1975 a new recreation centre was proposed for the Monyhull site, so that the activities organised for the residents could be co-ordinated and extended. After much discussion it was decided to convert one of the homes into a multipurpose centre. It was to have a club room, with easy chairs, coffee tables, bar, dance floor, stage, and a games room for darts, table tennis, snooker etc. Next to the club, there was a new centre shop selling a range of items for residents and staff. The "77" Club was officially opened in September 1978 by the Lord Mayor of Birmingham, and quickly became the social centre at Monyhull.

The centre also provided a room for play therapy and a toy library. This project was initiated in 1976, by a number of people including Dr. Baillie, Mrs Lawson, Psychologist, Miss Price, Social Worker, Sister Guise and the Revd. Dr. Easter. The project was developed as a result of the growing number of residents with severe and profound disabilities, whose social and educational needs were not being adequately met.

The aim was to provide play therapy for those severely handicapped residents who could not benefit from attending the workshops. Sessions were initially provided on a small scale, on a one-to-one basis, three times a week. After two years, twenty residents were benefiting from the play therapy groups, and those involved were "convinced of their value and importance to the growing number of severely subnormal patients at Monyhull" (Price 1978). By 1979, it was estimated that 150 residents could benefit from play therapy. As the equipment in the toy library and the demand for it increased, a loan system had to be introduced. A two day seminar on play therapy and groups was also provided, as the project took on hospital wide importance.

The working party's overall review of services concluded that:

> *"much thoughtful and conscientious effort was being put into patient training at Monyhull and its associated hostels. Training and recreational staff were enthusiastic and anxious to use their expertise to help enhance trainees' functioning and increase their enjoyment of life."*

However, it was felt that improvements could be made with a greater co-ordination of the existing resources and the provision of a wider range of educational and leisure opportunities for a greater number of residents. Although nursing staff provided the major input into the training, education and recreation of patients, it was recognised that greater input from specialist staff was also needed to meet the needs of residents, particularly as they became more dependent. This included more input from speech therapy, physiotherapy and occupational therapy. Difficulties in recruiting staff however, had meant that provision was severely limited. A district based speech therapist visited the hospital for only two half days a week. Physiotherapy services had been provided since 1975, but the department was not properly established until 1979. With only one fulltime physiotherapist however, it too could only offer a limited service. Unlike most hospitals, Monyhull had no occupational therapy department at all.

The working party recommended that further specialist staff should be recruited and their departments expanded, to meet the growing and changing needs of the residents. A multidisciplinary 'Training Team' was also to be established, with an 'Activities Programmer' to co-ordinate the needs of residents with the available resources. Furthermore, a new purpose built 'activities centre' was to be provided.

The Leisure Venture

In 1976, another project was being initiated to create a therapeutic outside environment which would offer a range of recreational facilities and opportunities for all of the residents. A multidisciplinary committee, chaired by the Revd. Dr. Easter, was set up to consider the scheme in detail. For the next six years, staff volunteers from all disciplines worked together with the support of the engineers, gardeners and other departments, to make the plan a reality. Funds for the project were raised in a number of ways by the hospital and the League of Friends.

By 1983, the area behind the "77" Club had been transformed. There was a patio, garden and seating area for barbecues and picnics; a pond for fish and ducks; an aviary and small animal and pets area. The garden project bloomed, with the growing of plants, flowers, vegetables and herbs, and an 'activity hill' was built, which became affectionately known as 'Easter's Folly'.

Resident working on the garden project.

Taking the goats for a walk.

The scheme did not stop there. With sponsorship from the Friends of the Earth and funding from the Manpower Services Commission, the Monyhull Leisure Venture grew from strength to strength. The funding meant that full time staff could now be employed to take responsibility for the day to day running and development of the venture. The scheme would also provide valuable work experience and education for local unemployed people.

The leisure area was developed into a free adventure play area for the more able residents, and a guided play area where those with more severe disabilities could experience a variety of stimuli. There was a specially designed tree seat and picnic table to assist people with physical disabilities. Paths for use by wheelchairs linked the different areas, and led to the activity hill so that the residents could enjoy the view and a picnic. A putting green was also introduced.

The project was officially completed in September 1984, but

continued to develop with additional funding. It now aimed to increase the involvement of residents and the local community in conservation and nature projects. Residents were involved in nature sessions, and worked on the garden or helped with the animals. Gardening was also introduced for those living in the community residences. The whole area was used by the hospital and the local community for social activities such as barbecues, fireworks and fun week.

From the beginning, it had been hoped that the Monyhull Leisure Venture would:

> *"provide a blueprint for similar ventures both nationally and internationally, demonstrating the need for society to plan and design facilities that can be used by mentally handicapped people as well as other groups. The project thus seeks to pioneer the development of aids for the mentally handicapped at the same time as providing a community facility as a natural means of integration."*

Through the vision, commitment and involvement of staff and residents, the Friends of the Earth, League of Friends and other local voluntary and community groups, the venture was able to achieve its aims and was regarded as a huge success.

Breaking Down Barriers

The White Paper had stressed the importance of involving voluntary groups and the local community in the life of the hospital. It was of vital importance to break down the barriers of prejudice and ignorance in the wider community and to promote acceptance and understanding of people with learning disabilities. The leisure venture, activities of the church, and the work of various voluntary groups had all proved how valuable and successful this could be. Monyhull also threw open its doors every year for a week of fun and fund raising with the Summer Festival. This had been a natural development of the annual sports day and fete held for the hospital in previous years.   In the summer festival programme of 1975 it was stated that:

SUMMER

FESTIVAL

AT THE

Monyhull Hospital
12th - 17th May '75

STAR ATTRACTIONS
★
Chris Tarrant of "Tiswas"
★

NUNEATON NUTTERS   STUNT CAR TEAM
ZIMRIYAH CHOIR — SINGING STEWARTS
POLICE DOGS   —   ARMY DISPLAYS
TRAMPOLINING   —   EXHIBITIONS
SIDE SHOWS   —   FOOTBALL

All proceeds from the Summer Festival will go
towards a Mini Bus for our patients.

This programme of events can only be used
as an admission ticket to the festival.
See Back for ticket details.

Programme - - - 10p
Children 5p

Monyhull summer festival programme 1975.

Presentation of the new minibus by Mr. Roy Hull Chairman of the Earl Foundation 1976.

"*although the hospital has a life of its own, it is also wide open to the community in which it lives. This implies interest and involvement by the surrounding community in the life and needs of the hospital and it is planned to invite people in to see and share, and to invite local groups to encourage patients to join them. The more barriers of ignorance and fear are broken down, the more effective treatment, education and care, in this hospital will be.*"

As well as raising awareness, the festivals served as an opportunity to raise much needed funds for the hospital. In 1975, the aim was to raise enough money for a minibus, to provide independent transport for the residents and so provide further opportunities for trips and holidays. A whole week of events was planned, with musical shows, football competitions, tug-of-war, police dog displays, stunt cars, bands, a funfair, and sideshows. There was also an exhibition of craft and art work by residents. The festival was opened by Chris Tarrant, of the television programme "Tiswas", and was a great success. The minibus was officially presented to the residents by Mr. Roy Hull, Chairman of the Earl Foundation, in 1976.

In the Jubilee year of 1977, Monyhull celebrated with a number of parties, a brass band, a fancy dress parade and competition, and a procession of decorated floats. A float was also entered in the Maypole May Week Carnival on the theme of "Springtime at Monyhull". Residents and staff helped to make the hundreds of paper flowers needed for the decoration of the float. The gardeners provided fresh flowers and plants.

"A tremendous amount of effort went into organising the decorated float...and we provided yet another opportunity for our patients to meet the outside community, and aroused a considerable amount of interest amongst other spectators along the route...The moment of judging came - the patients were bursting with excitement when we were told that Monyhull had won first prize, a trophy!" (Woods 1977).

The summer festival that year held an unexpected surprise for the residents. The Sunday Mercury reported:

"Senator Edward Kennedy has sent a personal letter of good wishes to launch Birmingham's Monyhull Hospital into its Jubilee Festival next Sunday. And if that's not enough to make a success of the event which aims to raise £2000 for a recreational centre for the mentally handicapped, a good luck message will also be coming on the day via an amateur radio satellite link-up."

"Mr. Leslie Blennerhassett, education officer for the hospital is the man behind the event, which will be opened by Birmingham comedian Don McClean. 'I wrote to the Senator about the event because I knew that his sister was mentally handicapped and he was very interested in the work done in this field' he said. The radio link-up, if everything goes according to plan, is thought to be the first of its kind for charity in Birmingham."

"From Senator Kennedy, part of the message reads ' To all in the West Midlands region involved with the mentally handicapped I send my personal commendation and

hopefully your festival will inspire others in the community to join with you in your humanitarian and rewarding endeavours."

By the end of the 1970s, Monyhull had become a much more open community:

"There is much more freedom for everyone these days. You can go out anywhere and speak to anybody. All this is very different from the old days...The hospital is much better today than in the old days and if they can go on improving it then good luck to them" (Jordan 1976).

It also had a much smaller population of residents, with different and greater needs than in the past. The changes envisaged by the Mental Health Act of 1959, were slowly coming to pass. Community services were expanding, and the role of the hospital as a centre for specialist services was becoming a reality. Then in 1981, the consultative document "Care in the Community" not only restated the government's commitment to a social model of care in the community, but for the first time also gave the mandate for complete hospital closure.

Chapter 8

"An Ordinary Life"

During the 1980s, a number of papers were published which advocated the expansion of residential accommodation in the community and the gradual running down and closure of long stay hospitals. One of the most influential papers was "An Ordinary Life" (1980) which looked at ways of developing a comprehensive model of residential care based on ordinary housing. The goal was:

> *"to see mentally handicapped people in the main stream of life, living in ordinary houses in ordinary streets, with the same range of choices as any citizen, and mixing as equals with the other, and mostly not handicapped members of their own community."*

In 1981, it was estimated that a third of people living in mental handicap hospitals could be immediately discharged into the community if appropriate alternative services were made available to them (DHSS 1981). The years that followed did in fact see a rapid expansion in private residential care, far exceeding the growth in local authority provision. Between 1980 and 1987, the number of residential care places increased by 11 000. This expansion however, was largely uncoordinated. During the same period, the reduction in hospital beds was even greater, estimated at 14 000. The result of rapid hospital discharge accompanied by a shortfall in the number of residential places available, and lack of adequate funding arrangements, meant that community care was soon in crisis.

There was also growing concern as to the quality of available community provision. Community care policies intended:

> *"to enable people to live as full and independent a life as is possible for them in the community for so long as they wish to do so. For many people, this means providing the services and support they need to continue to live in reasonable comfort in their own*

homes for as long as possible. For others, who may have experienced long stays in hospital and have more intensive care needs, it means helping them to re-establish their lives away from large institutional settings" (Kenneth Clarke 1989).

For many people, the move from hospital to residential housing undoubtedly meant a vast improvement to their lives. However, this was not always the case. Living in ordinary housing did not necessarily mean greater access to the opportunities enjoyed by the wider community. Nor did it necessarily mean acceptance by the local community or an improved quality of life. Without a high level of care and support, there was a very real danger that some people were becoming just as isolated in community settings as they had been in the old style institutions. Indeed there was growing opinion that in some instances, the more positive aspects of sheltered communities should be retained. Organisations such as RESCARE for example, advocated that small residential or village communities should be developed as an alternative to individual group homes in community settings.

In response to the growing crisis, the Griffiths Report (1988) attempted to resolve the various problems by recommending that social services take the lead in coordinating community care. They were to be responsible for the planning and delivery of individual care 'packages', carrying out a comprehensive assessment of needs, with input from health and other care agencies as necessary. Local authorities would then purchase appropriate services by drawing up contracts with the provider agencies. This would enable them to monitor the services provided and ensure that certain standards were being maintained. The provision of housing was to be separated from the provision of residential social care, and contracts were to be awarded to voluntary and non profit making agencies where possible. Health authorities were to continue to be responsible for specialist health services including any necessary input into assessing needs and delivering packages of care. The report recommended that mental handicap hospitals should close, but that:

"each closure needs approval, monitoring and control at the highest level. No person

should be discharged without a clear package of care devised, and without being the responsibility of a named care worker."

The recommendations of the Griffiths Report were to become reality with the passing of the NHS and Community Care Act in 1990. Two years later, a plan was unveiled to close all the remaining long stay hospitals, and resettle the remaining 25 000 people into ordinary community housing. In Birmingham, institutions such as Middlefield, Lea Hospital, Coleshill and Dean Hall gradually closed. Monyhull was finally targeted for closure in 1993.

Strategy for Change

For a number of years, the Regional Health Authority had been directing Monyhull to reduce the number of beds provided, whilst at the same time developing specialist support services for both the hospital and the community. This strategy for service change and development was based on a statement of values, which reflected the view that people with learning disabilities have the same human values and rights as anyone else. In planning terms this meant that people should use ordinary services wherever possible, with access to specialist support as and when required.

Changes in the organisation and management of Monyhull aided the process of service change and development. Historically, all the long stay institutions were the responsibility of the Medical Superintendent, who reported to the Board of Control. Following the 1948 NHS Act, Hospital Management Committees were formed, which at Monyhull included the Medical Superintendent, Matron, Chief Male Nurse and the Hospital Secretary. Management was now by consensus, but a rigid hierarchical structure was still firmly in place. In 1974, Monyhull became part of South Birmingham Health District, and so became part of a much larger organisation. In 1982, the District became a Health Authority in its own right and the Hospital Management Committee was replaced by a Unit Management Team. Monyhull was now subject to the overall direction and strategy of the Health Authority, and it was felt by many members of staff that it had "lost its identity" and the personal contact known previously.

The number of reorganisations in the Health Service and the changing social attitudes towards people with learning disabilities during this time led to a period of unsettlement and uncertainty at Monyhull. In 1986, the first General Programme Manager, Ms. Elizabeth Perkins, the District Clinical Psychologist, was appointed to take full responsibility for the Mental Handicap Unit. The appointment of a Clinical Psychologist as the overall manager of the service, reflected the move away from the traditional medical model of care towards a more social approach. It was important however, to retain a clinician in the post with experience and knowledge of specialist support services. The consequent developments in policy and practice initiated by Ms. Perkins over the following ten years led to a time of great challenge and change at Monyhull.

By 1994, the Unit had become the Learning Disabilities Directorate of South Birmingham Mental Health NHS Trust, and was managed by a Directorate Board. This comprised of Ms. Perkins, as Clinical Director, Mr Louden, Director of Nursing, Dr. Clarke, Consultant Psychiatrist, Mr. Rich, Director of Administration and Planning, Ms. Recchia, Personnel Manager, Mr. Kenny, Director of Estates, and Ms. Watson, Quality Manager. Changes in the organisation of the hospital followed, with the introduction of specialist units based on residents' needs. Multidisciplinary teams were formed to plan and develop services for people with challenging behaviour, multiple and profound disabilities, and the elderly, with separate teams to consider occupation and recreation. This was a move towards greater staff involvement in the planning and decision making process. It was vital for Monyhull to improve and develop its services, not only to provide the best possible care for the remaining residents, but also to establish itself as a specialist support and resource centre in the future.

The Regional Health Authority had charged Monyhull with the task of reducing its beds to 200 by 1992, whilst at the same time developing alternative community services. The Management Team did not however, regard the reduction in hospital size as an end in itself. Their over-riding objective was to ensure that people were resettled into places that provided for their individual needs, with the necessary levels of care and support.

A Resettlement Team was set up in 1986, to assess the needs of residents and ensure that discharges and residential placements were made appropriately. The team initially consisted of a senior nurse, social worker, and psychologist, with input from the other departments as required. Residents recommended for resettlement were assessed by the team as well as by the specialist support services, and multidisciplinary care plans were drawn up using the Individual Programme Planning process. The team were then able to recommend the type of placement, training needs and additional special requirements for each individual. In 1987, 45 per cent of residents were categorised as needing some form of long term residential care with a high level of support.

"A Poverty of Resources"

As more and more people were resettled into the community, it became possible to close some of the older and more unsuitable homes on the Monyhull site. These had been in use since 1908 and were no longer appropriate for the needs of the remaining residents. Indeed, some were in such a poor state of repair that they were literally falling down. Although there had been a continuous programme to upgrade and adapt the homes, limited resources meant that in reality only small improvements could be made each year. It had not been possible to provide small group homes for the remaining residents, in line with the principles of "an ordinary life." Instead, the majority still lived in the 'wards' built eighty years ago. The use of the term 'wards' still existed although many of the homes had since been given new names, such as Earlswood, Malvern, Brandwood and Norton. Others remained as Home 2 or Home 3, depending on the wishes of the residents. With the emphasis now on social care and a normal living environment, nursing staff no longer wore uniform and Monyhull had dropped the title of hospital.

The Unit Management Team assessed the situation in 1988, in a bid for additional Regional capital. They measured the quality of the

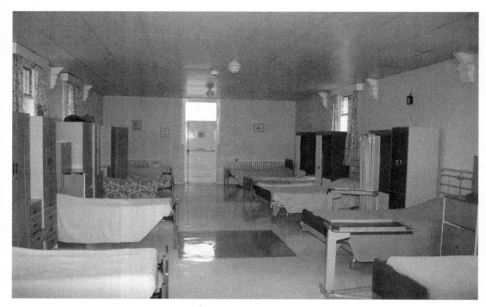

"Ward" for 25 men 1988.

home environment for the remaining residents against a list of agreed minimum requirements that constituted "the basic essential home comforts that the majority of people would expect." Each of the remaining 14 homes was assessed with the question "Would you want to live here?"

Despite the improvements made since the 1970s, the report was shocking. 57% of residents still slept in a dormitory with at least nine other people; no-one had sufficient room to store all their belongings; only three homes had sufficient armchairs for everyone to sit in. There were only 24 baths for over 300 residents, and in most cases there were no cubicles for people to wash in privacy. The report highlighted the "poverty of resources" and the resulting institutional conditions that people were still living in after all this time. It was not financially feasible to remedy all of the problems indicated, but additional resources were allocated by the Health Authority in response to the report which allowed for small improvements to be made. There was enough money to provide residents with personal wardrobes and an armchair; partitions were provided to allow for private sleeping arrangements; some of the homes could be redecorated.

Environmental and quality audits became a regular part of life at Monyhull. A quality team was established to monitor and evaluate the services provided, in order to improve the quality of life for residents. The Monyhull Audit Technique for Environmental Evaluation (MATEE) was developed for this purpose. The audits highlighted the problems faced by mental handicap hospitals everywhere, which were trying to adhere to the principles of normalisation, but were often without the capital to make the necessary improvements.

As in the past, improvements were small and slow to develop. The provision of a more homely atmosphere, personal belongings and privacy went some way towards improving the quality of day to day life for the residents. However, the only way significant improvements to the lives of the residents would be made, was by moving into small group houses in ordinary, non-institutional community settings .

Living room in a home for 16 people 1988.

Community Developments

Part of the Regional and District strategy for people with learning disabilities was the development of specialist support services in the community. Monyhull was the main provider of such services in South Birmingham, although it received no additional funds for this purpose until it was actually targeted for closure.

In spite of continuous financial constraints, Monyhull had been responding to the changing needs of the community. In the 1970s, it became increasingly apparent that many families were struggling to care for their mentally handicapped son or daughter, and were often trying to cope with the stresses and strains of full time care alone. A community nurse service was therefore established, providing support, active help, advice and counselling to people with learning disabilities and their families or carers in the South Birmingham district. They worked alongside the family and other agencies such as social services, GPs, and adult training centres, and provided an important link between the hospital and community services.

The Community Nursing Teams expanded in response to increasing need, particularly as more and more people were discharged from hospital. They worked closely with the social work department at Monyhull in this respect. This collaboration led to the formation of five Community Mental Handicap Teams. The new service comprised a community nurse and social worker, with the involvement of parents, carers and members of other disciplines and agencies as necessary. It provided a service for both children and adults in the South Birmingham area and was the first point of contact with the specialist services. These teams later became the model for Community Learning Disability Teams throughout Birmingham.

The teams helped to prevent unnecessary hospital admissions as Monyhull was now admitting people on a short term basis only. Although aiming to reduce the number of beds onsite, it was recognised that there was a very great need to provide a respite service to families in the community, who might not otherwise be able to cope with the strain of full time care. In 1982, Kingswood, a new purpose built short term care unit, was opened. It had 24 beds for people who needed both planned and emergency short term care for many different reasons eg. family holidays, general respite, medication reviews, assessment and treatment. Day care places were also available. Referrals by the community nurses or social services were taken for families from all over Birmingham.

Two years later, following a successful bid for Joint Funding by Ms. Perkins, a Community Challenging Behaviour Team was also established. This was a new specialist service for people with challenging behaviour and/or mental health problems, who required additional help and support to enable them to remain in the family or residential home. The team also provided counselling, advice, and comprehensive training courses for carers and staff members.

Before the implementation of the Community Care Act in 1990, and in recognition of the growing need for residential care, Monyhull had also begun to establish several of its own community residences. This was seen as a natural development of the pre-discharge units and hostels of the 1950s and 60s. Although these houses were managed and monitored by the Mental Handicap Unit, they were very much independent of the hospital. Residents, with the help of staff to support them, were able to live more independently in small 'group homes' and used the same community facilities, local GP, pharmacy and medical services as anyone else. For some people, this was the first time they had been able to enjoy 'an ordinary life'. In the words of some of the residents:

"After a period of about one week we had soon settled into the sort of things we had to do such as house work and other routine work that had to be done. At Christmas with the help of our guardian, we prepared and cooked the dinner which consisted of turkey, boiled and baked potatoes, sprouts, carrots, cranberry sauce, bisto gravy and Christmas pudding and custard. We realise how lucky we are to be here with a homely atmosphere, to come and go as we please; in other words we are a happy family...We wish it could have happened a long time ago" (Holton, Mann, Fisher and Vale 1984).

"At Christmas we all had a very nice happy day...All the cooking was done by Susie as we had a rest that day. We had some visitors like Mr. Easter, Mrs. Brick and Brian

Shanahan to see how we were getting on...I played Brian Shanahan dominoes for a cup on Christmas Day and I won 2-1 which was very good for me. We had plenty of presents to open and had a lovely day. I have been at Monyhull for forty years but it is far better being here" (Mann 1987).

The older hostels were eventually to close. The Cottage became a community unit for children, and Trostry became home to the District Psychology Service. The Haunch and Agatha Stacey were both demolished.

The day hospital at Monyhull was also to close. Instead, day services were provided at West Heath Day Centre, which later became known as Collingwood. This was a joint development between South Birmingham Health Authority and social services to provide adult education, training, and more intensive, specialist support. A small number of places were still provided in the training areas at Monyhull for those who needed them.

Specialist Support

This expansion of community provision meant that Monyhull could develop its role as a centre for specialist services. Specialist teams and support services encompassed various disciplines, including psychiatry, nursing, psychology, pharmacy, physiotherapy, occupational therapy, speech and language therapy, dietetics, education and chaplaincy. During the 1980s, these services had expanded in response to the increasing and changing needs of the residents.

When Monyhull was opened as a colony in 1908, it was the Medical Superintendent who took responsibility for the health and social needs of the residents, and the overall management of the institution. This continued under the 1948 NHS Act, which stated that all 'mental deficiency' hospitals were to have a Chief Officer who was a medical practitioner. Although these regulations were revoked in 1960, many of the long stay hospitals continued with a consultant psychiatrist as the overall manager. At Monyhull, the role of the medical staff began to change in the 1970s, when a more multidisciplinary social approach to care and treatment was introduced. Junior doctors took responsibility for the day to day medical needs of the residents, while specialist input and support was provided by the consultants, both at the hospital and in the wider community. The three consultants who provided this service in 1998 were Dr. Clarke, Dr. Prasher and Dr. Thinn. A pharmacist was also employed in the 1960s, to dispense and monitor medication; a role which was further developed by Mrs. Wilcher who provided support and advice to staff and residents on the effects of a wide range of drugs, including antipsychotics, antidepressants and anticonvulsants.

The role of the nurse at Monyhull had also undergone significant changes over the years. Qualified nurses and unqualified 'attendants' were initially custodians or guardians, who governed all aspects of the lives of the residents. With the move towards social care, training and rehabilitation in the 1960s, they took on the role of 'educators', helping residents to learn and practise daily living and social skills in preparation for discharge. As the resident population at Monyhull began to change, there was an increasing number of elderly and physically disabled residents who required a high level of care and support in all aspects of their lives. There were also a greater number of residents with a challenging behaviour and/or mental illness. Nursing staff therefore began to provide more specialist health care and support. By September 1998, the nursing establishment, managed by Mr. Louden, Director of Nursing Services, consisted of around 230 people, working both at Monyhull itself and in the community residences.

The clinical psychology department was established at Monyhull in the 1940s, gaining national and international recognition under Dr. Gunzburg, and expanding to become the largest of its kind in the country. By the 1960s, developments in social skills education, training and rehabilitation at Monyhull were being studied and adopted by mental deficiency hospitals across the UK and abroad. The department became a district wide service for people with learning disabilities and mental illness following the NHS reorganisation of 1982 and the appointment of Ms. Perkins. It then became the main provider of psychological services for all client groups, including

Self expression through painting.

children and the elderly. At the time of writing, the psychology service is part of South Birmingham Mental Health Trust. Services to adults with learning disabilities, managed by Mr. Richens, have included psychological assessment and treatment, comprehensive training programmes for staff and carers on the management of challenging behaviour, and specialist input to the resettlement process.

Chaplains have been providing for the religious and spiritual needs of the residents since Monyhull opened ninety years ago. The service flourished in the 1970s under the Revd. Dr. Easter, and, with the help of the Roman Catholic and Free Church chaplains, soon became involved in all aspects of hospital life. In 1972, the Bishop of Birmingham referred to Monyhull as "arguably the oldest ecumenical project in the city." The chaplains worked together to provide friendship to the residents, helping them to develop greater self expression and choice, and become more actively involved in the wider community. They also helped people in the local community to become more involved in the lives of the residents; breaking down barriers of fear and ignorance, and forging friendships and understanding. Pastoral support and advice has also been given to relatives, carers and staff members. More recently they have provided specialist input to planning and resettlement issues.

Many of the other support services only became established in the 1980s, due to serious recruitment problems. Some, such as speech and language therapy and dietetics, were contracted in on a sessional basis from other NHS Trusts. The rest were provided directly by the Learning Disabilities Directorate at Monyhull and South Birmingham Mental Health Trust.

The occupational therapy department has been amongst those most seriously affected by staff shortages. The department was initially established in 1980, next to the physiotherapy department in one of the purpose built workshops. A specially designed and equipped kitchen was installed some years later, to help residents develop daily living skills in a more realistic setting before

Physiotherapists at work (With kind permission from The Birmingham Mail).

resettlement. The department provided a number of group and individual programmes to help prepare residents to leave the hospital and to enable them to live more independently. However, difficulties in recruitment meant that in 1991 the service had to be split, with the living skills service provided by the Child and Family Centre, and the wheelchair and seating service by Oak Tree Lane. The current service managed by Mrs Boer was established in 1994, again to focus on daily living skills training and the resettlement of residents.

The physiotherapy department was established in 1979 by Mr Sathyaseelan. In 1982, Mrs Last, a remedial gymnast, was also employed to provide additional exercise and recreational therapy for the residents. Although initially two separate disciplines, the two combined in 1987, to form an expanded physiotherapy department with a gymnasium and soft play facilities. The new department, managed by Mrs Last, provided exercise and recreational programmes, electrotherapy, surgical appliances and walking aids, and help and advice on pressure relief and manual handling. It was also involved in a wide range of sports and leisure activities for residents including hydrotherapy, ski-ing, keep fit, and a sports club.

All of the support services have been involved in the assessment of residents for resettlement (where their specialist input was required), and in the Individual Programme Planning (IPP) process, which produces multidisciplinary care plans. They have also played a vital role in the planning and development of hospital based and community based services. An increasing amount of time is now being spent in providing services in community settings, including visits to the family or residential home, and adult training centres.

Sporting Success

Although many staff members now spent more and more of their time providing services in community settings, they also worked hard to enable the remaining residents to enjoy a better and more varied life at Monyhull itself. One of the most successful developments was in the field of sport. Many residents had been actively involved in sports since Monyhull opened, with weekly football and cricket

Monyhull Sports Club 1988.

matches, and annual sports day races and games. When the annual sports day was replaced by the summer fetes and fun weeks in the 1970s, and the weekly football and cricket matches began to diminish, there were fewer opportunities for residents to become involved. The situation was to change however, with the establishment of the remedial gymnastics department who formed the Monyhull Sports Club. Under the guidance of Mrs Last, Head Physiotherapist, more and more residents were encouraged to participate and compete in sports and physical recreation. There were now opportunities to join in activities such as circuit training, athletics, swimming, hockey, basketball, football, and ski-ing, and residents were encouraged to train for competitions. Mrs. Last became the chairman of the Birmingham Special Olympics Committee with Mr. Last (then Director of Nursing at Monyhull) as treasurer.

The involvement of Monyhull residents in the Special Olympic Games had actually begun in 1979, when Harold Silvers, a former day patient, made the team for the Special Olympic Games in France and the USA:

Enjoying a ski-ing holiday 1988.

"The French games held at Versailles are now history. The team representing England was entirely made up of competitors from the West Midlands and virtually won all that it could, even the cup for the best turned out team. Harold's personal haul was two gold medals and one bronze and his life since then has been a round of official lunches with various civic dignitaries, and photographs taken with his work mates and management" (Shanahan 1979).

In 1980, Mr Shanahan, a nursing officer at Monyhull, took the West Midlands team to the games in Belgium, and returned with 5 gold, 3 silver and 2 bronze medals. In the years that followed, and with the help and support of staff and volunteers, the number of residents from Monyhull competing in regional sports days and Special Olympic Games increased, and many more medals were won:

"Four gold, six silver and two bronze medals would be a creditable achievement for any nation's athletes taking part in the Olympic Games which Birmingham hopes to stage in 1992. So the Birmingham team which took part in the recent Special Olympics for the mentally handicapped can justifiably feel a sense of civic pride at their impressive

Another gold medal winner. West Midland Games 1990.

haul of medals. The Special Olympics, held earlier this month in Brighton, attracted over one thousand athletes from the United Kingdom, Ireland, France, Germany, Belgium, Denmark and the United States. Stars of the Birmingham contingent included Thomas Moore, winner of the pentathlon; Calfax Skyers, gold-medalist in the 50 metres; Vaseleky Paylou, who won the wheelchair soft ball throw; and the victorious relay team of Ian Edwards, Stephen Teasdale, Anthony Hamood and Thomas Moore. Most of the team came from Monyhull Hospital or nearby hostel accommodation. Participating in their favourite sports against an international field is, for them, a highlight of the year to look forward to, as it is for the staff who volunteer enthusiastically to accompany them." (Dines 1986).

The opportunity to compete in these games and competitions helped residents experience a much wider world away from Monyhull. It also gave the participants, the hospital and the local community a sense of pride at their outstanding personal and team achievements, putting the focus firmly on people's abilities rather than their disabilities.

Targeted for Closure

Although Monyhull had been discharging and resettling residents since the 1970s, it was not actually targeted for closure by the Regional Health Authority until 1993. In September 1994, South Birmingham Health Authority produced a Consultation Document outlining the proposed closure, resettlement of residents and the relocation of services in the community. Four options were to be considered:

1. "Do nothing" and retain the hospital service in its current form.
2. Complete relocation of all services from the Monyhull site, made possible by the development of a network of new community based services.
3. As option 2, but with the possibility that limited services, for example respite care, might remain on the hospital site.
4. Substantial redevelopment of at least part of the Monyhull site as a 'residential community' for people with learning disabilities.

The Health Authority proposed the third option, stating that:

"A substantial development of new community services would need to be in place before existing hospital based services were closed. In particular, residents would not be discharged until the right accommodation was available for them in the community, along with the necessary staffing and professional support services."

"This option would build upon the considerable experience of developing new services for people returning to Birmingham from hospitals outside of the city. In recent years, those people returning have included people with severe learning and other disabilities, who needed similar levels of care to the people living at Monyhull Hospital. Many successful resettlements have been arranged with, it is felt, those people now enjoying a greatly improved quality of life."

"The intention is to provide people with 'homes for life', with levels of support being flexible enough to accommodate people's changing needs."

A three month consultation period followed which included meetings for staff at Monyhull which were attended by representatives from the Health Authority Purchasers and Birmingham Social Services; meetings for the relatives and carers of long stay residents; meetings with the Kingswood House Parents Group; discussion with the Community Health Council; written responses from individuals and organisations; and discussion with the national organisation, Values Into Action, who represented the views of the residents.

The consultation period led to wide ranging and sometimes heated debate:

"Varying views about the future of services for people with learning disabilities were expressed, both at the consultation meetings and in written responses. What united respondents was concern for the well-being of the people living at Monyhull or using existing services there, and the desire to see the best possible future for these people. Continued uncertainty is causing considerable distress to residents, their relatives/carers and to staff at Monyhull and this is keenly felt." (SBHA 1995).

There was however, little doubt that Monyhull, as an institution, would finally close. In the words of one staff member:

"To be honest, there is no real option over the closure of Monyhull. Government policy and the Regional Health Authority have decreed that 'Thou shalt be closed'. The discussion should be about how this is to be accomplished." (Wilcher 1994).

Chapter 9

Planning for the Future

The closure plans were received by residents, parents, relatives and members of the staff and public with mixed sentiments. For some it was simply a natural progression of policies based on the principles of normalisation, which had led to more and more residents being resettled into the community. Closure was the inevitable step to 'letting go' of an out dated model of care. For others, it was seen as a 'cruel blow' to the remaining residents, many of whom were now elderly, and for whom Monyhull had always been home. They believed that the majority of these residents would not enjoy a better quality of life upon leaving the hospital.

There was a collective response to the closure document by the relatives and carers of people living at Monyhull or receiving respite care at Kingswood House. Over the years, many had come to believe that the kind of sheltered environment and care provided by Monyhull was essential for their relatives' needs:

"Like most parents, I guess, I had thought I could never contemplate my son ending up in a place like Monyhull. Such places have a poor image, and even though I know one mother who was very pleased with her son's lifestyle there, I share the usual prejudice against this form of care, taking it for granted that institutionalisation would be the result. I couldn't have been more wrong."

"Monyhull is a remarkable place when you get to know it inside, and it has the potential to develop into a first class community for handicapped people, provided it is not meanwhile destroyed by cuts and by what I now think are the wrong policies ie. the drive to so-called 'community care' for everyone. No doubt there are many for whom these policies are appropriate, but that is not always the case."

"I am convinced that places like Monyhull are essential. Some handicapped persons who could not cope with city streets, can develop considerable independence and wander

round the 'campus' in safety. Some who could never go shopping on their own, learn to handle their own money in the Centre Shop and the '77 Club with the caring assistance of the staff. Some who would undoubtedly meet with prejudice and misunderstanding in public places, can find friendliness and acceptance in the 'village' community while making closer friends in the homes. Their lives are less restricted and more fulfilled than the lives of similar handicapped people in the so-called community, which is not a community but a conglomerate mass of people riven with social problems and dangerous traffic." (Young 1985).

Relatives asked that new bungalows be built on the Monyhull site, to enable social links and friendships between residents to be maintained. This would also mean that people who had lived at Monyhull for most of their lives would not have to move to completely new surroundings. In addition, they asked that existing staff, who had built up close relationships with the residents, be retained in the new residences. The importance of retaining the respite service at Kingswood House was also stressed.

This was a view shared by many, including the Community Health Council (CHC) who stated:

"In essence the CHC supports the closure of Monyhull and the development of community based services which facilitate the resettlement of many of Monyhull's current residents. However, the CHC wishes to see part of the Monyhull site retained for the provision of respite care (Kingswood House) and for the development of a small number of small residential units to provide accommodation for some of the current residents for whom resettlement may not be in their best health or social interests."

The Clinical Advisory Team at Monyhull, with members from the psychology, chaplaincy, quality, education, physiotherapy, occupational therapy and pharmacy departments, were generally in favour of closure, but held the following concerns:

"Firstly, it must be stated that we think the movement from a hospital institution to a family home in the community ought to be an enriching and life enhancing experience for our people, and we are therefore in favour of such a move in principle. Secondly, because of the complicated nature of our residents' needs and because they have spent most of their

adult life - and in some cases their whole life - in institutions, it will need to be done slowly and sensitively. They are frightened of change and of the unknown, and so far we have been unable to reassure them or their relatives as to the kind of care they can expect."
(Wilcher 1994).

Some staff were also worried about the levels of acceptance and understanding to be found in the wider community:

"I hope things will be better and society is kind to them. When the fire alarm used to go off, people used to think that someone had escaped. People are ignorant. They sometimes cross over the road rather than walk past the driveway."

"It's got to be better, but this place protected them, and now they won't have that protection."

Overall, staff members supported the resettlement of residents into ordinary homes in community settings, but were concerned about the process of closure and its effects upon the residents. Moving home is considered to be one of the most stressful of life experiences, and many residents were showing signs of distress and worry about the future. One resident responded to the closure proposals by saying that he would only leave Monyhull upon his death.

It was therefore vitally important to involve the residents as much as possible in the consultation and planning process. The organisation Values Into Action, was commissioned to spend time with a number of the residents and report upon their views and feelings about closure. Many residents were found to be very anxious about the future. Some of the older residents wanted to stay at Monyhull, in familiar surroundings and with their friends. The idea of sleeping alone in their own bedroom after 60 years of sharing a dormitory was considered almost to be a 'punishment'. For them, Monyhull had always been and always would be their home. It was again proposed that new bungalows be built on the Monyhull site, within view of the remaining residents. The need to maintain friendship groups was also stressed.

Other residents were keen to move out, and were looking forward to the changes in their lives. When asked where they would like to live in the future, there were various responses:

"Not a hospital. Somewhere nearby, with other people."

"Ladies and men together. A detached house with Christmas lights and Christmas trees, a coal fire and nice food."

"A flat somewhere outside where I can cook my own meals myself. Is that easy to cook your own meals yourself?"

Members of staff were also suffering from stress, uncertainty about the future and their jobs, and a sense of impending loss. Like many of the residents, some had spent the whole of their working lives at Monyhull. One staff member said that "working at Monyhull is like being part of one large family and now that family is slowly dying." It was not generally considered possible to ensure that staff moved with the residents. The Directorate was not to be a major provider of residential or social care, and many staff were faced with the prospects of reapplying for jobs in the new services, redeployment within the Trust, voluntary redundancy or early retirement. Some of the nursing and care staff who provided services for elderly, and/or disabled residents, or residents with challenging behaviour would be able to transfer under 'Transfer of Undertakings' (TUPE) arrangements to the new care providers. All staff were given the opportunity to attend counselling and training programmes to help cope with effects of the closure.

South Birmingham Health Authority considered the responses to the consultation document, and agreed to an extended version of option three. This included the reprovision of six purpose built bungalows on the Monyhull site, a respite care service, an assessment and treatment service for people with challenging behaviour, and a community resource centre for the specialist support services. Plans were then drawn up to ensure that the remaining residents be resettled and the whole site cleared by February 1997.

Specialist Health Care Services

South Birmingham Mental Health NHS Trust was formed in 1994 to provide mental health and learning disability services to the population of the West Midlands and beyond. The following mission statement set out the aims and objectives of the Learning Disability Directorate:

"To provide the highest quality health and other services to people with a learning disability including people who have additional mental health problems, epilepsy or physical disabilities. The service is based on treating each of its clients as an individual with human rights to dignity, opportunity and choice and seeks to assist each of them to lead a valued life."

"This means the services will strive to ensure the participation of each individual in social and community life; enable individuals to undertake all the activities of daily life; promote in each individual, confidence, skills and experience, no matter how severe their disability; deal with each individual with respect and courtesy."

The last Management Committee at Monyhull 1998.
(L-R) Dr. David Clarke, Senior Lecturer in Psychiatry, Elizabeth Perkins, Clinical Director, Stuart Rich, Operations Manager, David Louden, Director of Nursing Services, Giosi Recchia, Personnel Manager.

"The directorate believes that as far as possible client needs should be met by provision of the mainstream health and social services. Specialist health care professions are required to support people in accessing such ordinary provision and to provide specialist services to a smaller number who cannot use ordinary services."

"Specialist health care services should be provided in a community setting. These services should be of high quality based on 'best practice'; the services should be accessible and responsive to individual needs, and adaptable to future client needs. The directorate will enhance its own services by drawing on the clinical skills and experience of its staff and, in recognition of its natural lead role, will offer clinical leadership to agencies providing care for people with learning disabilities." (Directorate Board 1998).

Following the proposals for the closure of Monyhull, the Directorate had to manage the gradual closure of the hospital whilst continuing to provide high quality care for the remaining residents, and developing specialist services in the community. Additional funding was made available by the Regional Health Authority for this purpose.

By 1998 business plans for the following services had been drawn up and accepted by the Purchasers:

1. A specialist community support service, comprising psychiatrists, psychologists, paramedical and support staff, to be provided for people with learning disabilities in South Birmingham. It is to be based at Kingswood House on the Monyhull site, which will also provide accommodation for the managers and administration staff for the new services.

2. A ten place assessment and treatment service including specialist respite care, to be provided for people with learning disabilities who also have a mental illness and/or challenging behaviour. This is to be located in a refurbished Brookfield House.

3. The respite care service currently provided from Kingswood House, is to be reprovided for people with learning disabilities and their

families in South Birmingham, in two newly built bungalows off the Monyhull site.

4. The provision of a Pan-Birmingham mental impairment service, (under discussion).

The closure of the hospital was not to affect the other services currently provided by the Directorate off the Monyhull site. These included the services provided at Collingwood Day Centre, the community residences, (including those for people with challenging behaviour), and the Community Challenging Behaviour Team.

Inevitably, the timetable for closure slipped and at the time of writing it is expected that the remaining residents will be resettled and the reprovided services in place by the end of the millenium.

Birmingham Health Authority has also decided that from April 1999, a Pan Birmingham Learning Disability Service will be provided, combining the services of the Learning Disabilities Directorate with that of the South and North Birmingham Community Trusts.

A New Home

All of the remaining residents at Monyhull are now being resettled into new homes in ordinary houses in the wider community, in Birmingham and beyond. Each person has had their individual needs assessed and reviewed by a joint Resettlement Team, formed by the North and South Birmingham Community Trusts and Social Services. Full involvement has been made of the staff at Monyhull, parents, relatives, residents and their advocates. The assessments have encompassed all aspects of the residents' lives, including accommodation requirements and preferences, staffing levels and skills, day and leisure activities, and specialist health needs. A pre-discharge planning meeting ensures that as far as possible, appropriate arrangements are made to meet these identified needs.

Resettlement groups have been made based on existing friendships and relationships at Monyhull. It is of vital importance that friendships and relationships built up over the years at Monyhull

Enjoying the garden.

are respected and maintained. Residents will move into purpose built or adapted group houses provided by housing associations. Staff and care services will be provided separately by care agencies working in partnership with them. In general, residential care will not be provided by South Birmingham Mental Health Trust, which will concentrate on the provision of specialist support services. This however, does not include existing residential provision or services for people with challenging behaviour.

The resettlement programme has been phased and based upon planned home closure. This has not necessarily meant that the people living in the homes due to close first, were the first to be resettled. Some residents have therefore found themselves moving internally within Monyhull, before moving into their new homes. Although these moves have been kept to a minimum, they have inevitably added to the distress and uncertainty that many residents were feeling about their future.

Concern about the impact of the closure upon the residents led to the setting up of a three year Resettlement Advocacy Scheme in June 1996. This was a project developed by Citizen Advocacy South Birmingham Area (CASBA), and funded jointly by Birmingham Health Authority and Social Services. CASBA itself, was established in 1989 at the instigation of a multidisciplinary forum at Monyhull. It aimed to assist people with learning disabilities to find advocates, who could encourage and support them to become more independent, and take more responsibility for their lives. CASBA's Monyhull project aimed to help residents make informed choices about their resettlement and be as fully involved as possible in all aspects of the assessment and resettlement process. With the help of two part time advocacy workers based on the hospital site, residents have been encouraged to express their views, feelings and preferences about the move from Monyhull and their wishes for the future. The advocacy workers have then attended review meetings with residents or on their behalf, or helped people write letters to the resettlement team with their views. They have also been involved with the Occupational

A canal boat holiday.

*Former residents getting married.
(with kind permission from Elizabeth Ralph).*

Therapy Department in running groups to help people come to terms with the move and become more familiar with using community facilities. This resulted in the setting up of a self-advocacy group to allow people to talk about their feelings. Although most of the residents were looking forward to the move and the changes to their lives, many were still uncertain and worried about what was happening.

Residents have been given help, support and practical training, both as individuals and in small groups, to prepare for discharge. They have been gradually introduced to their new homes and carers, to help make the move less stressful and frightening. Residents who have already moved to their new homes, have in general found the experience to be a positive one.

In 1999, the remaining 124 residents will be living in their new homes in ordinary houses, using the same local facilities - transport, shops, restaurants, pubs, GP's, pharmacies - as anyone else in their street. They will have the necessary support to help them lead their

At the pub.

lives as fully as possible, and will have access to specialist services and more intensive support if and when required. They will no longer be the patients of a hospital, but ordinary citizens of their local community.

Redeveloping the Site

When Monyhull Colony was established in 1908, the site and farms covered 185 acres. As the years passed, land was gradually sold off for housing developments and the site diminished substantially. Today, Monyhull covers around 79 acres of land, which has been sold for redevelopment. About half of the area is planned for new housing with open recreational space and a village green. The

Holiday in the sun.

Birmingham Plan for the site acknowledges that the:

> *"Proposed rationalisation of Monyhull hospital will provide major opportunities for development. In the short term it is proposed to develop the site for housing and land adjacent to Chinn Brook will be transferred to public ownership to protect and enhance its nature conservation and wildlife habitat value. This will form a green walkway between the canal and the City boundary adjacent to Moundsley Hall. In the longer term, further sites are likely to become available for new houses and associated uses. Additional educational facilities are likely to be provided through the expansion of existing schools."*

The redevelopment of the site will provide some 300 to 400 new homes "of all sizes and types in an attractive and safe environment". A new junction is planned to provide access to the site and help alleviate the increased traffic flow in the area. The main drive to the hospital, an 18th century carriageway, will be retained as a footpath and cycle path, to link the new housing development with existing residential areas beyond the Chinn Brook. 30 per cent of the site is planned for public open space, including two football pitches and a centrally located neighbourhood park and equipped play area. This will include the land developed by the staff at Monyhull which formed part of the Leisure Venture project, with the old activity hill, 'Easter's Folly' as the focal point. Proposals have also been put forward for an area of shopping and recreational facilities on the frontage with Monyhull Hall Road.

Areas of archeological interest are to be retained. Medieval remains within the Chinn Brook Valley include a burnt mound, medieval fish pond, and evidence of ridge and furrow cultivation. There may also be further remains below ground. The Nature Conservation Strategy for Birmingham (1996) has also identified land near to the Worcester and Birmingham Canal and the Chinn Brook to be of particular environmental value. Some development however, has been planned for the Stratford-upon-Avon Canal, to:

Visiting a wildlife sanctuary.

"capitalise on those characteristics which define and provide interest along and adjacent to the canal and promote opportunities to create housing, working and leisure environments of unique value and quality for Birmingham residents, workers and visitors."

The rest of the land has been designated for specialist health care use, including the provision of respite care services, assessment and treatment services, and a specialist resource centre. Service developments are now well underway. The six new purpose built bungalows for some of the remaining and more elderly residents are almost complete. Some of the hospital buildings have already been demolished. Only Brookfield and Kingswood houses, St. Francis Church, the nursery and Monyhull Hall will be retained. Monyhull Hall is a grade II listed building and is to be restored.

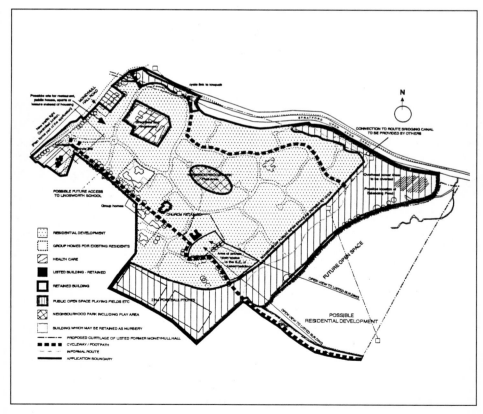

Plan of the redevelopment scheme at Monyhull 1997.

Epilogue

"Let There Be Light From Anew"

At the turn of the century, awareness became focused on the "plight of the mental defectives" who were suffering from neglect, exploitation and abuse in the workhouses and poor law institutions. To protect them, and to protect society at large, the Royal Commission advocated the establishment of special institutions or colonies to provide custodial care and social supervision. Initially, these colonies aimed to provide treatment and training for people to develop the skills necessary to live in and be of value to the local community. However, following the 1913 Mental Deficiency Act and the process of certification, they became places of segregation and confinement. The 'colonists' were excluded from the wider community and soon became institutionalised.

Over the years, it became recognised that with additional care and support, people with learning disabilities could lead full and valued lives in the wider community. The passing of the 1959 Mental Health Act began the long journey away from confinement and institutional care towards a supported social model of care in the community. During the 1960s, considerable developments were made in the fields of social education and training, medicine and pharmacology, which enabled people to live ordinary lives outside of the long stay hospitals. The principles of normalisation and an ordinary life were widely becoming the basis for service policy and provision. Over the next twenty years, more and more people were discharged into the community, despite the lack of adequate alternative facilities. The resulting crisis led to the Community Care Act of 1990, which attempted to resolve the problems by allocating further resources and passing over the responsibility for care to the social services. It also recommended the closure of the old style long stay hospitals, which no longer have a place in today's society.

In 1908, Mr. R. J. Curtis founded Monyhull Colony to provide and care for "sane epileptic and feebleminded persons" from the Birmingham, Aston and Kings Norton Unions. It was considered at the time to be a 'bold venture' and acted as a pioneer in the treatment and care of people with learning disabilities across the country.

Monyhull gradually changed from being a closed, selfcontained and selfsufficient community based on custodial care and control, to an open but 'sheltered environment', for its residents. Developments reflected and sometimes informed changes in attitudes and legislation towards people with learning disabilities. By the 1960s, the focus was very much on the active training and rehabilitation of residents for life outside the hospital. The work of Dr. Earl, Dr. Stanley, and Dr. Gunzburg in particular made Monyhull one of the most progressive mental deficiency hospitals in the country at the time.

However, a continuous lack of resources hampered service provision and development. Despite all the progress which had been made, the residents at Monyhull continued to suffer from the effects of staff shortages, overcrowding, and institutional conditions. In the face of no alternative however, the hospital continued to play a positive role in their lives. It has taken almost thirty years from changes in legislation, attitudes and the advent of normalisation principles, for comprehensive provision and support in the community to be established.

Monyhull is finally due to close in 1999. After ninety years of care and treatment, one of the oldest long stay hospitals for people with learning disabilities in the country will cease to exist. The remaining residents will have moved into their new homes, specialist health services will be reprovided in community settings, and the Monyhull site will be redeveloped to provide new homes for a new neighbourhood. As one community comes to an end, so another springs up in its place. It is time to let go of the past and look to the future.

References

Alaszewski, A. (1986). *Institutional Care and the Mentally Handicapped*: The Mental Handicap Hospital. Croom Helman.

Bailey, B. (1988). *Almshouses*. Robert Hale, London.

Bainton, C., Dewhurst, R., and Jones-Owen, W. (1979). *Monyhull Patient Training and Recreation. A Working Party Report.*

Birmingham, Aston and Kings Norton Joint Poor Law Establishment Committee (1905-12). *Proceedings.*

Birmingham, Aston and Kings Norton Joint Poor Law Establishment Committee (1908-9). *Resolutions.*

Birmingham, Aston and Kings Norton Joint Poor Law Establishment Committee (1909-1912). *Monyhull Colony Reports.*

Birmingham, Aston and Kings Norton Joint Poor Law Establishment Committee (1913). *Monyhull Colony for the Care of Epileptic and Feebleminded Persons. Souvenir of Foundation Stonelaying.*

Birmingham, Aston and Kings Norton Joint Poor Law Establishment Committee (1921). *The History of Monyhull Colony.*

Birmingham City Council (1996). *Nature Conservation Strategy for Birmingham.*

Birmingham City Council (1997). *Development Brief. Monyhull Hospital.*

Birmingham Mail (1940). *Nuisance Attacks. Many Bombs Dropped in Midlands.*

Birmingham Regional Hospitals Board, Hospital Management Committee, *Monyhull (1958). Monyhull Hall Commemoration of the 50th Anniversary of the Opening of the Hospital.*

Birmingham Regional Hospitals Board, Hospital Management

Committee, Monyhull (1959). *Monyhull Hall Training Workshops Booklet.*

Birmingham Regional Hospital Board. Hospital Management Committee, Monyhull. (1960). *Monyhull.*

Blennerhassett, L. E. (1995). Monyhull Colony: *A Brief Account of the Ethos, Aims and Achievements of a Sheltered Community.*

Carlin, M. (1989). Medieval English Hospitals. In *The Hospital In History*. Ed. L. Granshaw and R. Porter. Routledge.

Carter, C. A. (1911). The Guardians of the Poor. In *Birmingham Institutions. Lectures Given at the University*. Ed. J. H. Muirhead.

Clarke, K. (1989). *Statement to Parliament on the Future Arrangements for Community Care*. D.o.H. Press Release.

Coventry Trainers in Disability Issues (unpublished). *The History of Disabled People: Six Centuries of Segregation.*

Curtis, R. J. (1914). *Poor Law and the Care and Training of Mentally Defective Persons*. Poor Law Conferences 1913-14.

Curtis, R. J. (1922). The English Poor Law System and the Work of the Birmingham Guardians. In *Birmingham Poor Law and Workhouse Miscellaneous Documents* Vol. 1. Birmingham Reference Library.

DHSS. (1971). *Better Services for the Mentally Handicapped*. HMSO.

DHSS. (1981). *Care in the Community - A Consultative Document on Moving Resources for Care in England*. HMSO.

Dines, A. (1986). *Birmingham Athletes Win Olympic Gold*. South Birmingham Health Authority Press Release.

Earl, C. J. C. (1956). Simplicity. *Journal of the Midland Mental Deficiency Society* (2).

Goodger, H. (1990). *Kings Norton*. Brewin Books.

Griffiths, R. (1988). *Community Care: Agenda for Action*. HMSO.

Gunzburg, H. C. (1959). In Memoriam. C. J. C. Earl. *Journal of the Midland Mental Deficiency Society* (9).

Gunzburg, H. C. (1970). The Hospital as a Normalizing Training Environment. In *Advances in the Care of the Mentally Handicapped.* (1973). Ed. H. C. Gunzburg.

Hands, H. (1982). A Residents View. *Monyhull Link Magazine.*

Hill, F. (1998). Written Memories of Monyhull.

Holton, F., Mann, K., Fisher, K., and Vale, N. (1984). Our Group Home. *Monyhull Link Magazine.*

Hull, R. (1976). Mr. Raymond Jordan. In *New Aspect Quarterly Magazine for the National Society for Mentally Handicapped Children, West Midlands Region.*

Jay, P. (1979). *Report of the Committee of Enquiry into Mental Handicap Nursing and Care.* HMSO.

Jordan, R. (1976). My Life Story. In *New Aspect Quarterly Magazine for the National Society for Mentally Handicapped Children*, West Midlands Region.

Kay, M. (1976). The Evolution of Nurse Training. *Monyhull Link Magazine.*

Kings Fund (1980). *An Ordinary life: Issues and Strategies for Training Staff for Community Mental Handicap Services.*

Knowles, D. and Hadcock, N. (1971). *Medieval Religious Houses, England and Wales*. Longman, London.

Lawson, A. (1978). An Analysis of Responses Given to the Kings Fund Centre "Living in Hospital" Questionnaire.

Lethbridge, J. P. (1993). *Birmingham in the First World War*. Newgate Press.

Lock, A. B. (undated). *The History of Kings Norton and Northfield Wards*. Midland Educational Company, Birmingham.

Mann, K. (1987). Christmas Day at Haunch Lane. *Monyhull Link Magazine*.

Manual for Mental Deficiency Nurses (1936-7). Bailliere, Tindall and Cox.

Midland Mental Deficiency Society (1952-3). *Annual Proceedings*.

Miles, L. (1978). From the Heart. *Monyhull Link Magazine*.

Nirje, B. (1970). The Normalization Principle - Implications and Comments. In *Advances in the Care of the Mentally Handicapped*. (1973). Ed. H. C. Gunzburg.

O'Brien, J. and Tyne, A. (1981). *The Principle of Normalisation. A Foundation for Effective Services*. CMH.

O'Hara, J. (1967). *The Role of the Nurse in Subnormality. A Re-appraisal*. Fred Esher Award Essay.

Percy, Lord (1957). *Report of the Royal Commission on the Law Relating to Mental Illness and Mental Deficiency, England and Wales (1954-7)*. HMSO.

Price, Z. (1978). Play Therapy Groups. *Monyhull Link magazine*.

Radnor, Lord (1908). *The Report of the Royal Commission on the Care and Control of the Feebleminded. (1904-8)*. HMSO.

Reports of the Commissioners of the Board of Control (1914-48).

Reports of the Matron, Monyhull Colony (1915-21).

Rogers, C. A. P. (1972). *Looking Back. A History of Monyhull*.

Rooff, M. (1957). *Voluntary Societies and Social Policy*. Routledge and Kegan Paul.

Shananhan, B. (1979). Success Story. *Monyhull Link Magazine.*

Snape, J. (1975). Progress in Fashions for our Patients. *Monyhull Link Magazine.*

South Birmingham Community Health Council (1994). *Response to the Consultation Document on the Proposed Closure of Monyhull Hospital and on the Consequent Development of Services for People with Learning Disabilities in Birmingham.*

Smith, A. (1960). *The History of the Nursing Profession*. Chatto and Windus, Cambridge.

South Birmingham Health Authority, Mental Handicap Unit Management Team (1988). *The Quality of the Environment at Monyhull Hospital.*

South Birmingham Health Authority (1994). *Consultation Document on the Proposed Closure of Monyhull Hospital and on the Consequent Development of Services for People with Learning Disabilities in Birmingham.*

South Birmingham Mental Health Trust, Learning Disabilities Directorate (1998). *Mission Statement.*

Stanley, R. (1959), (1961). Report to the Hospital Management Committee, Monyhull.

Stanley, R. (1963). A Social Survey of the Hospital Population. *British Journal of Mental Subnormality* (11).

Sunday Mercury (1975). *Kennedy Sends His Blessing to a Hospital.*

The City of Birmingham Mental Deficiency Act Committee (1933). *Monyhull Colony. Commemoration of the Twentyfifth Anniversary of the Opening of the Colony.*

Tredgold, A. F. (1908). *Textbook of Mental Deficiency*. Bailliere, Tindall and Cox.

Tredgold, R. F. and Soddy, K. (1963). *Tredgold's Textbook of Mental Deficiency*. 10th Edition. Bailliere, Tindall and Cox.

Watkin, B. (1975). *Documents on Health and Social Services. 1834 to the Present Day*. Methuen and Co.

Wilcher, M. (1994). *Response to the Consultation Document on the Proposed Closure of Monyhull Hospital and on the Consequent Development of Services for People with Learning Disabilities in Birmingham.*

Woods, B. (1977). The Pro's and Con's of Entering a Float in a Local Carnival. *Monyhull Link Magazine.*

Young, F. M. (1985). *Inside Monyhull.* Birmingham Mencap Year Book.

Index

X

Y
Yardley, D 79,90,99

Z